Mathematics in Retrospect

Studies in the Evolution of Mathematical Thought and Technique
Written for those who would cultivate Mathematics either
as a Vocation or as an Avocation

*

THE BEQUEST OF THE GREEKS

by Tobias Dantzig

NUMBER, THE LANGUAGE OF SCIENCE

FORM

ASPECTS OF SCIENCE

A LA RECHERCHE DE L'ABSOLU

HENRI POINCARÉ, CRITIC OF CRISIS

TOBIAS DANTZIG

The Bequest of
the Greeks

New York

CHARLES SCRIBNER'S SONS

1955

Library of Congress Catalogue No. 55-7193

Printed in the United States of America

TO DR. VANNEVAR BUSH

GRAND MAN OF AMERICAN SCIENCE

The Bequest of the Greeks is a study of problems, principles and procedures which modern mathematics has inherited from Greek antiquity. Not all the ideas and issues which had agitated the great Greek minds, from Thales to Pappus, were destined to live. Some were still-born, others moribund, many withered on the vine, many more perished in the storm which all but obliterated the glory of Hellas. Much has been written on these topics, and this writer recognizes how important such studies in mathematical archaeology are to a comprehensive history of the field. However, *The Bequest of the Greeks* is not a history of Greek mathematics. It deals only with such issues as have survived the Grand Catastrophe, survived the long hibernation of the Dark Ages, survived even the growing pains of the Era of Restoration, and are alive today.

This work grew out of the author's experience with another book, *Number, the Language of Science*. Like that earlier work, the present volume is addressed to two categories of readers. Typical of the first group is the individual who has neither the preparation nor the taste for the technical aspects of mathematics, but who, upon reaching intellectual maturity, has come to realize its importance to contemporary thought and life. The gap in the mathematical education of such readers is more than offset by their eagerness to learn and their capacity of appraising and absorbing ideas.

On the other hand, there is the ever-growing group of people who have acquired a more professional attitude towards mathematics. The typical individual in this category is, temperamentally, interested more in the "how" than in the "why" of things. Thus, the origin and the evolution of the methods he uses in his daily work should be of real concern to him, inasmuch as this will help him to appraise the validity of these methods as well as their limitations. But this is not all. Some of the practices of the Greek mathematicians have passed into oblivion not so much because modern discoveries have rendered them obsolete, but because they were lost in "the shuffle of history." Indeed, quite a few of these practices excel, both in efficacy and elegance, the routines which the individual has learned on the school bench.

This desire on the part of the writer to reach two groups of readers, so dissimilar in attitude, taste and interest, accounts for the dual structure of the present work. Part One, *The Stage and the Cast*, is designed for the general reader, and no effort has been spared to stay within his mathematical ken. It is the author's belief that the average high school curriculum is fully adequate for this part of the work. Part Two, *Anthology of the Bequest*, is more technical in character. Indeed, most of the problems treated in the *Anthology* have only in recent times reached a stage of fruition, while some remain unsolved today. The reader with a penchant for mathematics will experience no difficulty with the principles implied; but a deeper understanding of these problems can be attained only through diligent exertion. In the words of Spinoza: "Omnia praeclara tam difficula quam rara sunt." *All that is excellent is as difficult as it is rare.*

The Bequest of the Greeks is the first of three volumes which will appear under the collective title *Mathematics in Retrospect*. The second volume, *Centuries of Surge*, will follow shortly: its thesis is the rebirth of mathematics and its prodigious progress in the seventeenth and eighteenth centuries. The concluding volume of the trilogy, *The Age of Discretion*, which deals with the development of mathematics in the nineteenth century, is in preparation, but the writing has not yet reached a stage when a definite date can be set.

The rest of this preface is the defence of a title. To describe in a few words the contents of a work is a difficult task at best, but when these words are to convey to the prospective reader the aims of the writer and the scope of his undertaking, then the task becomes formidable indeed. Yet, sooner or later, the writer of any book must face the problem of naming it. He passes in review a number of possible word-arrays, rejecting some because they err by excess, others because they err by default. In the end, he settles on a compromise, consoling himself that the preface may clear up the ambiguities of the chosen title.

PREFACE

The title *Mathematics in Retrospect* is not only ambiguous, it is ambitious as well. Indeed, the term "mathematics" embraces so vast a field of human knowledge that only the writers of an encyclopaedia would be entitled to use it as a title of their work, and the present work is not an encyclopaedia in any sense of the word. To be sure, the centrifugal trend of the author's mind did cause his interests to scatter in many directions; still, he found the more subtle aspects of modern mathematics beyond his ken or reach, with the result that such topics as topology, point sets, lattices, and many others too numerous to mention, will not be even touched upon. If, despite these gaps, the author resolved to use the title "mathematics" in all its bare audacity, it is because he could not find a more proper term to qualify the variety of topics handled in the book.

The phrase *in retrospect* is worse than ambiguous: it is susceptible of at least *three* interpretations. While the words suggest an historical approach, they could fittingly adorn the title page of a curricular survey, and just as fittingly be used to describe a book of reminiscences. Strangely enough, any of these seemingly contradictory interpretations could aptly apply to the present work.

For, though this work is not a history of mathematics, it does aim at restoring the historical perspective which the undergraduate curriculum has a tendency to distort. Thus, the historical approach has been freely used throughout in tracing mathematical ideas and processes to their sources and stressing, at the same time, the methods used by the masters of the past.

Again, while this book is not a review of an undergraduate curriculum, it does aim at integrating the experience of an individual who, after being exposed to these ideas and processes during a protracted but rather immature period of life, is about to plunge into the more advanced realms of mathematics incident to graduate study.

Finally, while this book is not a collection of reminiscences, the author has made no attempt to restrain the subjective element. Indeed, in a certain sense, this is the record of a man who for more than four decades has been studying mathe-

9

matics, teaching it, writing it, and applying it. Rightly or wrongly, the author cherishes the hope that this record will prove to be of some value to those who aspire to cultivate mathematics either as a vocation or as an avocation.

TOBIAS DANTZIG

Pacific Palisades
California
April, 1954

Acknowledgment

The author wishes to express his indebtedness to the Carnegie Corporation of New York for its generous assistance during the critical period in the preparation of this work.

Contents

PART I

THE STAGE AND THE CAST

THE STAGE AND THE CAST

Figure 1

Diophantus,(300AD) ⑮
Pappus, (300AD) ⑮
Ptolemy, 100AD-178 ⑯
Menelaus, (100 AD) ⑯

① Miletus, Ionia
② Samos, "
③ Chios, "
④ Athens, Greece
⑤ Delos, "
⑥ Cnidus, "
⑦ Crete, "
⑧ Crotona, Italy
⑨ Syracuse, "
⑩ Tarent, "
⑪ Elea, "
⑫ Rome, "
⑬ Elis, Greece
⑭ Abdera, Thrace
⑮ Alexandria, Egypt
⑯ Giza, "
⑰ Nazareth, Palestine
⑱ Tire, Phoenicia
⑲ Babylonia, Chaldea
⑳ Bagdad, Arabia
㉑ Perga, Pamphilia
㉒ Byzantium
㉓ Nicaea, Bithinia
㉔ Stagira, Macedonia
㉕ Carthage, Africa

=== Anno Domini ===

Hero, (100) ⑯
Theon, (130) ①
Nicomedes,(130) ㉑
Diocles, (130) ㉑
Hipparchus, (160) ㉓
Apollonius, (200) ㉕
Erotasthene, 276-194 ⑮
Archimedes, 287-212 ⑨
Aristarchus, 310-230 ②
Euclid, (300) ⑮

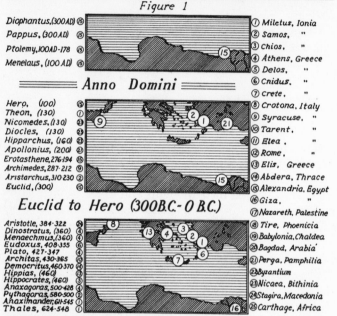

Euclid to Hero (300 B.C. - 0 B.C.)

Aristotle, 384-322 ㉔
Dinostratus,(360) ④
Menaechmus,(360) ④
Eudoxus, 408-355 ⑥
Plato, 427-347 ④
Archytas, 430-365 ⑩
Democritus,460-370 ⑭
Hippias, (460) ④
Hippocrates, (460) ③
Anaxagoras, 500-428 ④
Pythagoras, 580-500 ②
Anaximander, 611-545 ①
Thales, 624-548 ①

Thales to Euclid (600 B.C. - 300 B.C.)

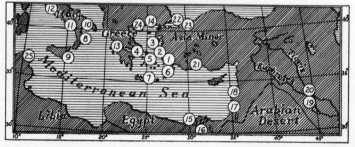

Chapter One

ON GREEKS AND GRECIANS

A dazzling light, a fearful storm, then unpenetrable darkness.

EVARISTE GALOIS

I

The stage on which were enacted the early episodes of the drama which I am about to unfold was Ancient Greece; the cast bore names unmistakably Greek; and the medium through which they conveyed their thoughts and deeds to their peers in culture was Greek, even though some of the records of these thoughts and deeds have passed through Latin and Arabic translations before reaching us. In these records we find the germs of theories and problems which have agitated the mathematical world ever since, and of which some remain unsolved to this day. We are told, indeed, that in mathematics most roads lead back to Hellas, and thus a book which makes any historical pretensions at all must needs begin with the question: Who were these *Ancient Greeks?*

The term conjures up in our minds a group of Aryan tribes, which had originally settled on the southern part of the Balkan Peninsula and adjacent islands of the Aegean Sea; then, spreading out in all directions, eventually reached the shores of Asia Minor, Lower Italy and the African littoral. The insular character of the land and its maritime activities encouraged independence and local rule; yet, dwelling as these people did at the very gateway of Europe, and menaced as they continually were by Oriental encroachment, they were often driven to "totalitarianism" as a means of self-preservation. Thus Ancient Greece became the proving ground of that struggle between oligarchy and democracy which has prevailed to this day; and as such we know it best.

But this is just one aspect of the complex pattern which the term evokes in our minds. In Ancient Greece stood the cradle of our culture: literature and philosophy, architecture and sculpture, in the various forms in which these arts are cultivated today, all had their origin in Greece. The songs of her poets, the works of her sculptors and the tracts of her philosophers are not mere monuments of a glory that was, but sources of study and inspiration today and, probably, for many centuries to come. Nor was the genius of these people limited to the arts and letters; their penetrating insight into the mysteries of number, form and extension had led them to develop to a high degree of perfection a discipline which they named *mathematics*, and which was destined to become both the model and the foundation of all sciences called exact.

This pattern becomes even more amazing when we contemplate that all this magnificent culture was erected in a few short centuries. We are told, indeed, that this great intellectual upheaval had reached its peak in the fifth century B.C.; that soon afterwards a general and rapid decline had set in, as though a fatal blow had been struck at the very roots of the mighty tree, a blow from which it never recovered; that after lingering on for a few more centuries, vainly endeavouring to live up to the grandeur of its past, it had finally succumbed to the *coup de grâce* administered by rising Rome.

2

Such is the picture of Ancient Greece as we perceive it through the thick historical fog of two thousand years. It is a perplexing picture, to say the least, for, as far as we know, nothing that ever happened before, or since, has even remotely resembled it. It is a picture of a people numerically insignificant, even when measured by standards of the Ancient World, which in the course of a few centuries erected a civilization of unprecedented magnitude, bequeathing to mankind for all time to come immortal treasures of literature, philosophy and mathematics. And the mystery becomes even more profound when we attempt —as is indeed our duty—to appraise this past in the light of the present. For the modern representatives of this ethnic group, far from exhibiting the acumen and finesse of their illustrious forebears, have contributed so little to the intellectual and artistic life of our time that it is difficult to conceive of any kinship between this Balkan people and the intellectual giants to whom our culture owes so much.

Is there anything wrong with this picture? Could it be that it is but another cliché, one of the many synthetic products of the diversified industry which passes today for liberal education? Well, this much is certain: in so far as the history of mathematics is concerned, this conception of Ancient Greece calls for a wholesale and drastic revision.

3

To begin with, the mathematical activity of Ancient Greece reached its peak during the glorious era of Euclid, Eratosthenes, Archimedes and Apollonius, a time when Greek letters, art and philosophy were already on the decline. There is a modern counterpart to this singular phenomenon. It was in the sixteenth century, the age of Cavalieri, Cardano, Galileo and Vieta, that mathematics was reborn; and the resurgence took place when the renaissance in arts and letters had already run its course, and the very names of Dante and da Vinci had become memories. Galileo was the central figure of that era, and the fact that he died one week before Newton's birth has been the subject of much historical comment. It is as significant, perhaps, that Galileo was born in 1564, within a few months of the death of the last great representative of Italian renaissance, Michelangelo.

In the second place, while Roman contributions to mathematics were less than negligible, there is no evidence whatsoever that either the Republic or the early Empire had in any way hampered its progress. The eclipse of mathematics began with the Dark Ages, and the blackout did not end until the last Schoolman was shorn of the power to sway the mind of man.

Lastly, it was not Greece proper but its outposts in Asia Minor, in Lower Italy, in Africa that had contributed most to the development of mathematics. Some of these outposts were Greek conquests, others had come under Greek domination through alliance or trade. Moreover, since the Greeks had no Gestapo to protect their Aryan blood from pollution, racial intermingling was widespread, and there is no evidence that these misalliances were frowned upon by Greeks of pure strain.

To be sure, the Greeks did divide mankind into barbarians and Hellenes; yet, scions of barbarian families who had adopted Greek names and customs were viewed by Greeks as Hellenes. Thales of Miletus is a case in point. From all accounts he was of Phoenician origin, as was, indeed, Pythagoras; still, not only was Thales classed by his contemporaries as a Greek but proudly hailed by them as among the seven wisest Greeks. As to his own attitude, listen to the words which one biographer puts in his mouth: "For these three blessings I am grateful to Fortune: that I was born human and not a brute, a man and not a woman, a Greek and not a barbarian."

In the centuries of Euclid and Archimedes Greek was the language of most educated men, whether they hailed from Athens, Syracuse, Alexandria or Perga. The significance of this will not escape the American observer familiar with the many melting pots strewn over this wide land. Could one assert that a man was of Anglo-Saxon blood because he was named Archibald or Percival and enjoyed a good command of English? Is it not equally naïve to contend that a man who lived in the third century B.C. was racially a Greek because he called himself Apollonius and wrote in Greek?

The shores of the Mediterranean harboured many a melting pot into which Greeks and Etruscans, Phoenicians and Assyrians, Jews and Arabs were promiscuously cast. Who can tell today how the Aryans and Semites had been apportioned within these seething brews, or the Hamites, or the Ethiopians, for that matter? The motley mash passed into the sewers of history without leaving a trace of its composition behind it. The distilled essence alone remains, bottled in vessels which bear Greek inscriptions.

5

"A dazzling light, a fearful storm, then unpenetrable darkness." So wrote Galois on the eve of his fatal duel; and if we did not know that he intended these words as a summary of his own short span of nineteen eventful years, we could take it as a description of the era of Hellenic mathematics.

What brought about this brilliant progress, and what caused the subsequent eclipse? I shall not add my own speculations to those of Taine and Comte, and Spencer, and Spengler and countless other historians of culture. This much is clear: mathematics flourished as long as freedom of thought prevailed; it decayed when creative joy gave way to blind faith and fanatical frenzy.

Chapter Two

THE FOUNDERS

To Thales . . . the primary question was not *What do we know*, but *How do we know it*, what evidence can we adduce in support of an explanation offered.

ARISTOTLE

I

Six centuries before the *zero hour* of history struck, there thrived on an Aegean shore of Asia Minor, not far from what today exists as Smyrna, a group of Greek settlements which went under the collective name of Ionia. It consisted of a dozen or so towns on the mainland, of which Miletus was the most prosperous, and of about as many islands, of which Samos and Chios were the largest. When measured by present-day standards, the territory was so small that if modern Smyrna were run by American realtors all that was once Ionia would be reduced to mere suburban "additions" to the "greater city."

Here, within the span of about fifty years, were born the two "Founders" of mathematics, Thales of Miletus and Pythagoras of Samos. According to some of their biographers both were of Phoenician descent, which seems plausible enough since most of the coast of Asia Minor was at that time honeycombed with Phoenician colonies.

2

Who were these Phoenicians? We remember them chiefly today as the inventors of the phonetic script which was so vast an improvement over all the previous methods of recording experience that, in principle at least, it has undergone no significant change in the twenty-five hundred years which followed. The

Greek *alpha*, *beta*, *gamma*, as well as the Hebrew *aleph*, *beth*, *gimel* are but adaptations of the Phoenician symbols for these letters.

And yet, having bestowed upon mankind this marvellous method of recording events, the Phoenicians left practically no records of their own, and what little we know of them today we owe to Greek or Hebrew sources. They were a Semitic tribe, and their homeland was what we call today Syria. As Canaanites, Moabites, Sidonians, they fill many a page of the Bible. Apparently, whenever they did not engage the Hebrews in mortal combat they fought them with subtle propaganda, inducing the fickle sons of Israel to abandon Jehovah for Baal and other more tangible gods.

The Greeks knew the Phoenicians under a different guise. They spoke of them as crafty merchants and skilled navigators, and called them "Phoenixes," i.e., red, because of the ruddy complexions which the Mediterranean sun and winds had imparted to these ancient mariners. For, the Phoenicians roved that "landlocked ocean of yore" from end to end, exchanging wares and founding colonies, such as ill-fated Carthage, or Syracuse, the birthplace of Archimedes, who, reputedly, was also of Phoenician descent.

3

I said that Thales was classed by the Greeks as one of the Seven Sages. Indeed, he was the only mathematician so honoured, and it was his reputed political sagacity and not his mathematical achievements that had earned him the title. Because of this distinction, Thales was the subject of many historical studies, with the result that much had been written on his life and deeds. Of what value are these biographical accounts? Here are some highlights from which you can draw your own conclusion.

We are told by one of these commentators that Thales was so keen an observer that nothing would escape his alert attention; yet, according to another, he was so absent-minded that even as a grown-up man he had to be followed on his walks by his nurse lest he land in a ditch. We are informed by one that he was a seasoned merchant in salts and oils, and that it was the pursuit of this trade that had taken him to Egypt; but another tells us that he had come to Egypt as a very young man, and that, struck by the learning of the priests, he had tarried among them for more than a quarter of a century, returning to Miletus in advanced middle age. According to one account he had learned all he knew of geometry from these very priests; according to another he was entrusted by the Pharaoh with the task of determining the height of the Great Pyramid, a problem which the priests had vainly tried to solve.

The accounts on his views, social, political or philosophical, are just as confusing. Some tell us that he was a confirmed bachelor, that he had found an outlet for his paternal instincts in adopting his sister's family, that once when asked why he did not marry and have children of his own since he loved children so much, he replied: "Just because I love children so much." Other biographers, however, assure us that Thales had married and lived to be a patriarch, surrounded by children and grandchildren. Plutarch holds that Thales had democratic leanings, in support of which he quotes his letter to Solon. There Thales invites Solon to make his home in Miletus, apologizing, at the same time, that his native city is under the rule of a tyrant. Again, once when asked what was the strangest sight his eyes had perceived, he allegedly replied: "A tyrant ripe in years." But other sources have it that upon his return from Egypt Thales made his home with the Milesian tyrant, that for many years he acted as the latter's counsellor at large, and that it was, indeed, on the advice of Thales that the dictator had wisely declined a tempting alliance with Croesus.

4

The accounts on Pythagoras may be less at variance, but they are bewildering enough in other respects, for, in addition to the confusing versions of the chroniclers, we have to contend here with disciples who would put into the mouth of their dead

Master anything that fitted an occasion or proved a point. Indeed, Pythagoras became the centre of a cult which persisted for many centuries and exerted a tremendous influence on scientific and religious thinking.

It is claimed that not only had he visited Egypt, but that his travels had taken him much farther East; that, in fact, much of the knowledge which he later conveyed to the Hellenes had been imparted to him by Persian Magi and the priests of Chaldea. One is almost willing to believe this after examining the medley of views and taboos ascribed to Pythagoras. Yes, *taboos*—since many of the rites of the sect later rationalized by his followers into principles have all the earmarks of taboos.

A case in point is the alleged Pythagorean aversion to animal flesh. I say alleged, for, on this score, too, there is no unanimity, some biographers asserting that Pythagoras celebrated his mathematical discoveries by sacrificing oxen to the gods, while others go so far as to claim that he was the first to introduce meat into the diet of Greek athletes who hitherto had been training on figs and butter.

Some followers of Pythagoras traced the interdiction to his doctrine of *metempsychosis*. According to them, the Master taught that of the three attributes of the soul only reason was exclusively human, while emotion and intelligence belonged to animals as well; that upon man's death his soul migrated from animal to animal; and that, consequently, by killing an animal one might mutilate a soul. All this makes beautiful reading but fails to explain why Pythagoras extended his dietetical prohibitions to beans. Indeed, according to Diogenes Laertius, this bean cult was the indirect cause of his death. Here is the story for what it is worth.

When Pythagoras returned from his Oriental travels, he found his native Samos under the rule of a tyrant. He then proceeded west and settled in Crotona, a prosperous city on the heel of the Italian Boot. There he eventually established a school and, incidentally, acquired great political power. Now, those were the days when totalitarianism was making serious inroads into Greek democracy, and so, as time went on, an opposition party arose which accused Pythagoras of dictatorial designs. A frenzied mob set fire to his mansion. The Master managed to escape, but having reached in the course of the ensuing pursuit a field of beans, he chose to die at the hands of his enemies rather than to trample down the sacred plants.

5

The reader will have realized by now what a formidable task it would be to pick the few sound kernels from this biographical chaff, let alone use the material to analyse the achievements of the Founders. And yet, behind the hazy mist of these fanciful tales and legends the portraits of the two men emerge, mere silhouettes perhaps, but silhouettes that become much less elusive and confusing when viewed as parts of the larger panorama of classical mathematics.

Neither Thales nor Pythagoras left any writings behind. In fact, the earliest mathematical work of any kind available to us today is Euclid's *Elements*. This does not mean that the mathematicians of the pre-Euclidean age had completely neglected to put their thoughts on parchment. On the contrary, *The Mathematical Roster* of Eudemus mentions two textbooks on mathematics written within one hundred years of Thales' death; one of Anaximander of Miletus, a pupil of Thales, the other by Hippocrates of Chios. However, these works, as many others of that period, were lost in the course of the next two thousand years. The same fate was shared by at least two works of Euclid, and by many tracts and treatises of the post-Euclidean period.

Now, most of these lost writings were still available in the fourth century A.D., when Pappus of Alexandria wrote his great book *The Synagogs* (Collection). What happened to this sizable literature? A few of these found their way to Arabia and were eventually restored to Europe, thanks to the enlightened care of Moslem scholars; others were destroyed when the great Alexandrian library was burned to the ground on the order of Bishop Theophilus, *Anno Domini* 392; still others perished in the darker ages which followed.

As a result, the only sources which could throw light on the pre-Euclidean period are some passages from the *Dialogues* of Plato; some casual remarks found in the writings of Archimedes, Apollonius, Hero and others; the *Collection* of Pappus which may be viewed as a sort of encyclopaedia of Greek mathematics; and fragments of an already mentioned essay on the history of mathematics written by a contemporary of Euclid, one Eudemus of Rhodes, as quoted by the Platonist commentator Proclus seven centuries later.

6

Unfortunately, Plato's opinions on matters mathematical were vitiated by a number of factors. In the first place, he was a Pythagorean *par excellence*. Try as he might, he could not free himself of the tendency to attribute most achievements in philosophy and in mathematics to either Pythagoras or his adherents. What is more, there is little evidence that he tried to free himself of that bias. Thus, we find Thales barely mentioned in the *Dialogues;* as to Hippias, Hippocrates and Democritus, who had either kept aloof from the School or had openly opposed it, they were treated with contemptuous silence.

In the second place, despite the vociferous claims of the Platonists and Neoplatonists, Plato was not a mathematician. To Plato and his followers mathematics was largely a means to an end, the end being philosophy; they viewed the technical aspects of mathematics as a mere device for sharpening one's wits, or at most as a course of training preparatory to handling the larger issues of philosophy. This is reflected in the very name "mathematics," a literal translation of which is a *course of studies* or, as we would say today, a *curriculum*. It was in this sense that the term was used in the Platonic Academy, and it was not until later that mathematics became the name of the science of number, form and extension.

What interested Plato most in mathematics were the metaphysical issues which lay back of its concepts. The very topics treated in the *Dialogues* give eloquent evidence to that effect. Thus, the so-called *Pythagorean proposition* which binds the sides of a right triangle received but casual treatment in the *Dialogues*, and even then the emphasis was on the number-theoretical aspects of the problem. On the other hand, such topics as *harmony*, *triangular numbers*, *figurate numbers*, and many other themes which we view today as more or less irrelevant, if not trivial, were taken up at length. Indeed, the guiding motive behind the mathematical predilections of the Pythagoreans and Platonists was of a type which the professional philosophers call *metaphysical* but which for the nonprofessional have all the earmarks of the *occult*.

7

The *Dialogues* were written more than one hundred years after the death of Pythagoras. In the course of these one hundred odd years the doctrines propounded by the Master had been vigorously attacked, first by the Ionian philosophers who followed in the footsteps of Thales, then by the Sophists who were led by Parmenides of Elea. The critique of the opponents and the defence of the proponents fill many an eloquent page of the *Dialogues*, and these vivid pages paint a far more convincing portrait of Pythagoras than do the extravagant tributes of his zealous followers.

These pages reveal a religious mystic who viewed number as the key to the plan which the Supreme Architect had used in fashioning the universe. Be it the movement of heavenly bodies or the composition of matter, the structure of thought or the principles of human conduct, everything was expressible in number because all was governed by number. It was the philosopher's mission to interpret the work of the Creator by deciphering, as it were, the intricate scroll of creation; but to do this, he must needs first master the code in which this scroll was written, and this code was mathematics.

"Number rules the universe." Did Pythagoras foreshadow in this dictum the vast system of formulae and equations by means of which modern science links the phenomena of nature, as Galileo foreshadowed it two thousand years later, when he wrote: "The universe is the grand book of philosophy. The book lies continually open to man's gaze; yet, none can hope to comprehend it who has not first mastered the language and the characters in which it is written. This language is mathematics; these characters are triangles, circles and other geometrical figures."

Or did Pythagoras conceive the scheme of creation as a sort of *supernumerology* which assigned to everything material or spiritual an integer, and reduced the relations between things to operations on these integers? Most of us today would view these two attitudes as irreconcilable, extolling the first as scientific and branding the second as occult. But to Pythagoras, and to his followers for centuries to come, the line of demarcation was by no means so sharp.

8

We find among the writings of the Pythagoreans such undisguised numerology as this: *two* being the number of *man* and *three* that of *woman*, *five* must of necessity be the number of *marriage*, since marriage is the union of the two sexes; or that *perfect numbers* are symbols of perfection, human or divine, since such a number is *the sum of its divisors*, hence self-contained and complete, i.e., perfect. In music, astronomy and geometry this numerology assumed more subtle forms. For instance, instead of representing a geometrical figure by a single number, the Pythagoreans assigned to it a *number type*. This accounts for their extraordinary interest in *triangular*, *square* and *figurate* numbers which appear so utterly inconsequential today.

But we also discover in the Pythagorean speculations more than a mere germ of what, for want of a better name, we call today the scientific attitude. That this attitude remained in an embryonic stage was due to the state of algebra at that time. Today, the representation of a physical law by means of a formula is so common that we accept it as though it were granted to man by Providence. But far from it being a gift from heaven, it was the culmination of a long and painful evolution, since even the most simple formula implies ideas which in the days of Pythagoras were either in their infancy or did not exist at all.

Indeed, in the first place, any formula postulates the existence of the *rational*, if not of the *real*, domain of numbers, while in the days of Pythagoras *number meant positive integer* and nothing else. In the second place, the reason we view the formula as the ultimate goal in the study of a phenomenon is because the problem is then reduced to the *routine operations of arithmetic and algebra* which most of us have learned on the school bench. Remember, however, that when about the year 1600 Vieta introduced literal notation, it struck even mathematicians as a sensational innovation; also, that even the operations of elementary arithmetic are barely more than five hundred years old; then transfer yourself in imagination to the sixth century B.C. when *rhetorical algebra* was in its very infancy, and *positional numeration* not even a dream. Again, before a formula linking the various entities can even be as much as formulated, it is necessary that these entities be *measurable*, or at least conceived as numbers; but in the days of Pythagoras, and for many centuries to come, such entities were hardly more than figures of speech or qualitative attributes.

Geometry was the one field where the transition from the *qualitative* to the *quantitative* stage was well advanced, and so it is not surprising that geometry became the proving ground for the Pythagorean number philosophy.

9

This brings us to the so-called *Pythagorean theorem*—the relation between the sides of a right triangle which we express succinctly today in the formula,

$$c^2 = a^2 + b^2.$$

I shall deal with the mathematical facets of this important proposition in subsequent chapters. Here, we are concerned with the historical aspects of this relation. How much did

Pythagoras contribute to the proposition which bears his name? Was he the discoverer of this property of right triangles? Was he the first to point out its far-reaching implications? Was he the first to demonstrate the theorem by logical arguments applied to the basic axioms of geometry? Well, such historical evidence as is available to us today suggests that all these questions be answered in the negative.

Pythagoras could not have been the discoverer of the relation, because, in one guise or another, this property of right triangles was known and used by scholars and artisans of Oriental lands thousands of years before Pythagoras was born. Indeed, we must bear in mind that while deductive geometry is barely more than twenty-five hundred years old, empirical geometry is probably as old as civilization itself. Many geometrical relations which were eventually confirmed by deductive reasoning had been known as experimental facts thousands of years before the Greeks began to cultivate geometry as a science. This is attested by much documentary evidence, such as the clay tablets of the Babylonians and the Egyptian papyri. But even more convincing is the mute testimony of the Pyramids and of the ruins of ancient edifices uncovered by archaeological research. Indeed, it is not conceivable that such structures could have been designed or erected without a considerable knowledge of practical geometry.

Again, if by proof of a mathematical proposition we mean establishing its logical validity on the basis of a set of assumptions accepted as self-evident, then Pythagoras did not possess a proof of the theorem which bears his name; not because such a proof was beyond the ken of his period, but because he was temperamentally uninterested in proofs of this nature, as may readily be gleaned from the methods which he used in his numerological deductions.

10

I am about to venture a conjecture, and I want to take the opportunity to emphasize that by advancing this and sundry other opinions which will appear in this work *I neither invoke authority nor claim originality.* I do not invoke authority, because in the absence of authentic documents opinion rests on imagination, and one imagination is as good or as bad as another. I do not claim originality, because to be valid such a claim would imply an exhaustive knowledge of the literature of the subject, and this would smack of omniscience. My position in matters of history is that one must either be prepared to substantiate a statement by reference to written records or else honestly admit that it is one's own conjecture and shoulder the consequences.

With regard to the Pythagorean theorem my conjecture is that at least in one of its several forms the proposition was known before Pythagoras and that—and this is the point on which I depart from majority opinion—it was known to Thales. I base this conjecture on the fact that the hypotenuse theorem is a direct consequence of the principle of similitude, and that, according to the almost unanimous testimony of Greek historians, Thales was fully conversant with the theory of similar triangles.

I do not contend that Thales was aware of the vast implications of this proposition for geometry and mathematics generally. These implications were not and could not have been fully appreciated until the advent of analytic geometry. But since, by the same token, Pythagoras could not have been aware of the geometrical significance of this theorem, the question as to whether he was the first to recognize the mathematical implications of the proposition which bears his name should also be answered in the negative.

On the other hand, there is no doubt that Pythagoras fully appreciated the *metaphysical* implications of this relation. For, the fact that the sides of a right triangle were connected by a law expressible in numbers suggested that all geometrical entities responded to such numerical laws, since, in the last analysis, any such entity could be viewed as an element of a rectilinear figure which, in turn, could be resolved into triangles, and any triangle was made up of right triangles. Thus this relation, which Euclid regarded as a mathematical theorem and which we construe today either as a postulate of geometry or as a ready consequence of other such postulates, was to

Pythagoras and the Pythagoreans *a basic law of nature,* and, at the same time, a brilliant confirmation of their number philosophy.

II

With the possible exception of Aristotle, no other philosopher of antiquity received as much publicity as Pythagoras. The spectacular character of the man, the fact that he was the titular head of a semi-religious cult and the acknowledged fountainhead of the Platonist School may explain his widespread fame. I spoke before of the extravagant claims made for him by his followers. These claims were not confined to the realm of mathematics. Among other things, he was credited with being the originator of the *heliocentric hypothesis*, in spite of the undisputable evidence that this hypothesis had been first propounded by Aristarchus, a contemporary of Archimedes.

The belief that Pythagoras had taught that the earth revolved about the sun persisted even after the contributions of Copernicus had been made public. In fact, in 1633, when Galileo was tried for his heresies, the immortal document of the Inquisition, in listing his errors, called the heliocentric hypothesis a Pythagorean doctrine. This brilliant subterfuge spared the Holy Office the embarrassment of indicting Copernicus, an ordained priest of the Church.

Today no one would think of associating Pythagoras with the Copernican theory; yet, although his discovery of the relation in a right triangle had no stronger foundation in fact, the idea that he was the originator of the theorem stubbornly persists. The result is that the name of Pythagoras is a household word to most educated people, while the name of Thales is known to but a few specialists, and even these regard him as a philosopher rather than a mathematician.

The Pythagorean theorem is by no means the only case when the honour for a capital achievement has been conferred on the wrong man, nor is mathematics the only field where such "miscarriages of justice" have occurred. The study of this phenomenon is a fascinating chapter in the history of thought

31

but lies beyond the scope of this book. However, as we proceed, we shall encounter other episodes of the kind which may cast some light on the underlying causes.

I would not advocate that the *Pythagorean* theorem be renamed *Thalesian*, even if I had sufficient documentary evidence to support my conjecture. The term "Pythagorean" has by now become a part of mathematical nomenclature. That this nomenclature is far from perfect, that, in fact, it bristles with misnomers, is generally recognized. Still, nobody seems to be able to do anything about it—not that reforms have not been proposed, but that almost invariably it was found that the effort required to effect the change by far outweighed the advantages gained.

12

The more one attempts to appraise the mathematical achievements of Pythagoras, the less impressive they appear. On the contrary, the more one studies the period of Thales—the more one compares the knowledge he bequeathed to posterity with the one he had found when he began his work—the more does his mathematical stature grow, until one is impelled to range Thales with such figures as Archimedes, Fermat, Newton, Gauss and Poincaré.

But while we cannot place Pythagoras among the great or even near-great mathematicians, his position in the history of scientific thought remains unchallenged. To be sure the dictum "Number rules the universe" might bring a condescending smile to the lips of a modern scientist: yet, forget the lofty form in which these words were put; conceive numbers not as just positive integers, as the Pythagoreans did, but in the broad modern sense of the term: then is there anything in the dictum to which a modern scientist could not or would not subscribe? The theories of relativity and quanta have shaken the physical sciences to their very foundation, forcing the physicist to cast overboard such principles as *conservation of energy or economy of action*, and to revise the very concepts of *space, time, matter, cause and effect*. Still, *number* reigns as firmly in the new physics as it did in the old. The argument that *the study of any phenomenon has not been consummated until the phenomenon has been made mathematically articulate* is as convincing today as it was in the days of Pythagoras whilst the conjecture that physical attributes may exist that are beyond the power of number to express would be as odious to the man of science today as it was to Pythagoras.

Chapter Three

ON THE GENESIS OF GEOMETRY

Geometry in every proposition speaks a language
which experience never dares to utter and of which,
indeed, it but half comprehends the meaning.

WILLIAM WHEWELL

I

Let us first of all dispose of some chronological matters pertaining to the era which, for want of a better name, we call classical mathematics. Sharing the average reader's keen dislike for dates, I shall confine myself to the "century posts" of that long and tortuous trail.

The year 600 B.C. finds young Thales in Egypt eagerly absorbing the knowledge of its priests: what appears to us as a maze of rules, recipes and rites amassed without rhyme or reason looms to the young Greek as a token of inestimable promise; 500 B.C.—Pythagoras is at the height of his glory at his school in Crotona; 400 B.C.—young Plato is fleeing Athens lest the fate of his teacher, Socrates, overtake him; 300 B.C.— Euclid's *Elements* usher in the great century of classical mathematics, the century of Archimedes and Eratosthenes; 200 B.C.—Apollonius completes his monumental treatise on *conic sections*; 100 B.C.—here, roughly, may be placed the birth of Hero of Alexandria; A.D. 100—here, roughly, may be placed the birth of Ptolemy; A.D. 200—darkness is already settling over the Hellenic world; Diophantus, then Pappus; last flickers of a dying fire, a fire which is not to be rekindled for another thousand years.

2

We are concerned here only with the first three centuries of this near-millennium; yet, this relatively short period is the

34

most perplexing in the history of mathematics. Not that it is so crowded with achievement or bristles with great names, as does the century that follows Euclid. No, it is not wealth of material but scarcity of information that forces a would-be interpreter of that period to resort to conjecture and speculation. The wisest course would be to dismiss the whole matter with a few summary remarks. Unfortunately, one cannot thus dismiss the fact that it was during these centuries that geometry had come of age; and so the story must be told, even if at the risk of some speculation and conjecture, and I know of no better way of telling it than by reversing the chronological order of events, proceeding in retrogress, as it were. Accordingly, I begin with Euclid.

He lived in Alexandria. These four words sum up all we know of the life of the man who was instrumental in shaping the mathematical education of countless generations, and one of whose works has had, next to the Bible, perhaps the largest circulation of any book ever written. No legends trail his name, and even the anecdoters have spared him. He was a prolific writer, yet only one of his works withstood the wear and tear of the centuries that followed him. The Greeks rarely referred to him by name: to them he was simply the author of the Στοχει, the work we call *Elements*, although *Basic Principles* would have been a more fitting translation of the Greek title.

The book was primarily a treatise on geometry, even though it did deal with other topics, such as perfect numbers, primes and irrationals. As a treatise on geometry it was so thorough that it serves to this day as the basis of most of our elementary textbooks. Still, comprehensive though it was, the *Elements* apparently did not express fully what Euclid knew on the subject, since at least two of his lost books also dealt with geometry. One of these, *Conics*, must have been an exhaustive study indeed, because when about a century later Apollonius came out with his own treatise on these curves, some of his more determined antagonists accused him of having plagiarized Euclid's work.

3

The title of the other lost book was *Porisms*, and all we really know about its contents comes from references to it by Pappus. This passage inspired Fermat to undertake a restoration of the lost work; unfortunately, the version of this great master of the seventeenth century suffered the fate of the original, as did several other attempted restorations, notably those of Wallis and of Simson.

Thus the only thing certain about the *Book of Porisms* is its title, and even here there is no general agreement as to the sense in which Euclid used the term. The literal translation of πορισμοσ is *method, means, implement*, and it is quite conceivable that Euclid meant just that, i.e., that the *Book of Porisms* was intended as a sort of supplement to the *Book of Elements*, that it implemented the fundamental principles expounded in the treatise by practical methods of construction. This would not contradict the assertion of Pappus that the book dealt with *loci*, inasmuch as the locus was the basic device of all Greek construction.

On the other hand, it is just as possible that the *Book of Porisms* was Euclid's contribution to those *celebrated problems of antiquity* which agitated the minds of all mathematically inclined individuals of his day. These problems were : *squaring the circle, doubling the cube, trisecting any given angle* and *cyclotomy*, i.e., *dividing a circle in any given number of equal parts*, the construction in every case to be executed *by the exclusive means of the straightedge and the compass.* or—what amounts to the same thing— by introducing no other auxiliary loci than *straight lines* and *circles*. The fact that none of these problems was mentioned by Euclid in the *Elements* would lead one to surmise that he had intended to deal with them elsewhere.

All these problems have been solved in modern times, i.e., solved in the "negative" sense, by demonstrating that the constructions cannot be executed within the restrictions imposed. The proofs require resources of algebra and analysis which the Greek mathematicians did not possess; this, however, could not have prevented a Euclid from surmising the truth, or from endeavouring to prove it by such methods as were at his disposal. Now, in the absence of an articulate algebra, the most natural approach to the question as to which constructions could be executed by ruler and compass and which could not was through a systematic study of geometrical procedures and of the loci which they generate, and, for all we know, it was just such a study that the author of the *Book of Porisms* had in mind.

4

This much is certain: Euclid had at his disposal a vast store of mathematical knowledge, particularly in the field of geometry. How much of this was his own discovery, how much the work of his contemporaries, or the bequest of an earlier age? There is irrefutable evidence that a substantial portion of the material recorded in the *Elements* was known before Euclid, and there is nothing either in the style or in the plan of the treatise to suggest that it was intended as a collection of original contributions. Thus, on the whole, it is safe to assume that the chief objective of the author of the *Elements* was to put system and rigour into the work of his predecessors.

Who were these predecessors? Well, the roster of the fourth century contains such names as Archytas, Eudoxus, Menaechmus, talented, even brilliant, men who undoubtedly had exerted considerable influence on the mathematics of their own period. It is unthinkable that their work had failed to influence Euclid as well, more particularly in his treatment of *solid geometry*. And yet, it would be equally erroneous to attribute to these men the discovery of the basic propositions of *plane geometry* which, after all, constitute the very lifeblood of Euclid's *Elements*, because all indications are that they had themselves inherited the rudiments of plane geometry from an earlier age. Indeed, unless they had these rudiments at their very finger-tips they could not have made the discoveries with which they were credited by subsequent commentators.

Let us tarry for a while on these achievements. Archytas is supposed to have been the first to study geometry on a circular *cylinder*, discovering in the process some of the properties of

37

its *oblique section*, the *ellipse*. Eudoxus was the first to study geometry on a *torus*, i.e., the surface generated by the circumference of a circle which revolves about an axis in its plane. He discovered the *sections* of this surface by planes parallel to the axis of revolution, *quartic curves* which today are called *Cassinian ovals*, after the French-Italian astronomer, Giovanni Cassini, who had advanced the theory that Kepler's ellipses were mere approximations, while the *true planetary orbits* were these very ovals. Finally, Menaechmus' claim to fame was the discovery of the *conics*, i.e., *the plane sections of a circular cone*.

Observe that all these studies involved three-dimensional considerations, despite that in each case the geometer had the properties of a plane locus as his avowed objective. It is as though he felt that the basic material of plane geometry had been exhausted, and that further progress could be achieved only by envisaging a plane locus ·as one *embedded in space*. But why did these geometers single out these special loci for their considerations? The answer takes us back to the celebrated problems which I mentioned in the preceding section, more particularly to that of *doubling the cube* which the ancients called the *Delian problem*.

5

The Delian problem was described with eloquence and humour in a letter which Eratosthenes addressed to King Ptolemy. The purpose of the letter was to present his own solution of the problem, a device which he called *mesolabe*. The following is a free translation of the opening paragraph of the letter. The complaint of Glaucos quoted by Eratosthenes comes from Euripides' lost tragedy *Poleidos*.

"An ancient playwright, describing the tomb of one hundred square feet which Minos had erected for Glaucos, put into the mouth of the latter the words, '*Too small hast thou built my royal tomb: double it but abide by the cube.*' Geometers long sought to determine how a given body may be doubled without altering its form, and called this problem Doubling the Cube.

There was much confusion for a while; at long last Hippocrates of Chios showed that the problem could be solved if one but knew how to insert two mean proportionals between a rectilinear segment and its double, whereupon one perplexity gave way to another no less perplexing.

"Then, the Delians, afflicted with a scourge, consulted an oracle who ordered that the altar in one of their temples be doubled. In their perplexity the Delians appealed to the geometers trained in the Platonian Academy, who zealously proceeded to solve the problem by seeking to insert two mean proportionals between two given segments. Archytas of Tarentum achieved this by means of a cylinder, and Eudoxus of Cnidus by means of the so-called oval curves. But while their methods lack nothing in geometrical rigour, their designs are not readily amenable to construction by hand . . . The design of Menaechmus is more handy, but it, too, is quite laborious."

6

Our backward march takes us next to the fifth century. Is this to be the end of our quest? Were the principles on which Euclid later erected his *Elements* discovered by the mathematicians of that period? No, the geometers of the fifth century seem to have been even less preoccupied with the rudiments than were those of the fourth. They, too, took the *Elements* for granted; they, too, were irresistibly drawn by the mirage of the unsolved problems. Indeed, if the fourth is to be called the Delian century of mathematics, the fifth was the century of the *circle-squarer*.

The lure of the quadrature problem was not confined to professional mathematicians like Hippias or Hippocrates; nor even to near-mathematicians, such as the philosopher Anaxagoras, teacher of Pericles, who, according to legend, had whiled away his time in prison by working on the problem. It attracted scores of amateurs and notoriety seekers. From all evidence, it was the fifth century that witnessed the emergence of that strange species whom Augustus De Morgan nicknamed *pseudomath*. This barnacle has clung to the hull of mathematics throughout its long and eventful voyage. It persists to this day.

Today, we identify the problem of squaring the circle with determining the *mathematical character of the number π*, on the ground that the area of the square sought is equal to πR^2. This reduces the quadrature problem to the construction of the segment πR, the segment R being given. Is the number *rational*, i.e., is π a solution of some linear equation with integral coefficients? If not, is it a solution of some *quadratic* equation, or of a chain of such equations? If not "quadratic," is it at least *algebraic*, i.e., is it a root of some *irreducible equation of higher degree?* Any number which is not a solution of an algebraic equation with integral coefficients is said to be *transcendental*. How difficult such questions might be, can be judged from the fact that it took nearly twenty-four hundred years to establish the transcendental character of the number π.

But what has the character of a number to do with the construction of a figure? Reserving a more satisfactory answer for a later chapter, let me say here that it may be shown that *if a number* n *is rational or quadratic, then the segment* nR *may be derived from the segment* R *by ruler-compass operations.* More generally, if *n* is an algebraic number, then it is possible to construct the segment *nR* by means of a more or less complicated *linkage*, i.e., by some device made up of rigid bars and pivots. However, *no linkage exists* which would permit one to derive *nR* from *R*, if *n* is a *transcendental* number; the mechanism would have to contain, in addition to bars and pivots, such members as *rollers, cams, gears*, etc.

When applied to the celebrated problems, these considerations permit us to conclude that since the number π is transcendental, *the quadrature problem cannot be solved by straightedge and compass, nor by any sort of linkwork*, for that matter; on the other hand, such problems as *the duplication of the cube, the multisection of a general angle, the division of a circle into any number of equal parts* are amenable to algebraic equations and can, therefore, be solved by means of linkages.

7

The major cause of the prevailing confusion in regard to such questions as the trisection of an angle or the squaring of a circle is *failure to discriminate between the problem of determining the character of a number and that of evaluating the number.* This confusion is by no means limited to laymen. Thus, writers who certainly should know better have asserted that the origins of the quadrature problem may be traced to China, Babylon or Egypt, when all they mean is that architects and surveyors of those ancient lands, confronted with the necessity of measuring circular arcs and areas, were led to assign some rational value to the number π.

Now, granted that attempts to evaluate the ratio of the circumference of a circle to its diameter are as old as empirical geometry, and that the latter is, probably, as old as civilization itself, such attempts have nothing to do with the problem of determining the mathematical character of π or with its geometrical counterpart, the squaring of the circle—problems which acquired meaning only after geometry had emerged from the empirical into the deductive stage. Even at that, there is doubt that such questions were actually raised during the earlier period of deductive geometry, since a precise formulation of these problems implies a thorough knowledge of the fundamental propositions of plane geometry, a mastery of its basic constructions and, above all, a critical attitude which comes only with advanced geometrical rigour.

We may be reasonably sure that the quadrature problem was born on Greek soil, and while we shall probably never know who first proposed it, it is certain that the event took place not later than the middle of the fifth century. Indeed, we know that the problem had inspired the efforts of the two mathematicians who dominate the second half of the fifth century, namely, Hippias of Elis and Hippocrates of Chios, the same Hippocrates who was mentioned by Eratosthenes in connection with the Delian problem. It was Hippocrates who first brought out that squaring the circle and rectifying its circumference were two horns of the same dilemma. Hippias went even further by devising a genuine "mechanical" quadrature of the circle, the only one of its kind in classical times, and one which for ingenuity, insight and rigour would do honour to an Archimedes.*

8

These are the facts: Hippias was born about 425 B.C.; Thales died about 550, after an active career which extended over almost half a century; it is reasonably certain that deductive geometry as such did not exist either in Greece or elsewhere prior to the birth of the Founder. Thus in less than two hundred years geometry had undergone a complete metamorphosis, changing from an Egyptian hodgepodge of rules of thumb to a full-fledged discipline.

This extraordinary progress becomes even more astounding when we reflect that, in so far as propagation of ideas is concerned, those two centuries were like two decades in our own time. Remember, indeed, that the habit of putting down one's thoughts in writing was practically nonexistent in those days; that such manuscripts as did live to see the light of day could be reproduced only by laborious copying; that mathematical nomenclature was in its infancy, and symbolism did not exist at all, since even the designation of vertices of figures by letters of the alphabet was not known before Hippocrates; that in the absence of a centre of mathematical activity such as Alexandria in the post-Euclidean centuries, mathematics was being cultivated in widely separated regions; that the exchange of ideas among scholars was largely by personal contact, and that a journey from Asia Minor to Lower Italy, which today can be accomplished in less than three hours by plane, required then many a month.

And this is not all. When these two centuries are viewed in the light of actual achievement, they dwindle into at most one, for the span of one hundred and twenty-five years which separates Thales from Hippias was particularly barren of mathematical progress. Indeed, it produced only one mathematician of note, namely Pythagoras, and he and his disciples

* See Chapters 10 and 11.

had been too preoccupied with the occult and metaphysical aspects of mathematics to contribute much of value to geometrical technique.

Thus the conclusion is fairly forced upon us that this prodigious achievement was the work of one man: Thales of Miletus. "He endowed geometry with rigour, and founded it on congruence and similitude"—such is the generous testimony of one historian. But this appraisal is not generous enough, for, he also implemented these principles with a rich technique, and taught how to apply this technique to construction and proof. That it took the Greeks more than a century to absorb the work of the Founder becomes less surprising when we contemplate the grandeur and revolutionary character of his achievement and remember that there were no geometers when Thales began: Thales the *teacher* produced the first geometers, even as Thales the *thinker* founded the first geometry worthy of the name.

9

The alternative theory offered in explanation of the rapid growth of Greek geometry is that much of the achievement claimed for the Greeks was actually of foreign origin. This theory is relatively new; as a matter of fact, any such contention would have found little support among the historians of science of the nineteenth century. To be sure, classical commentators on mathematics had been rather vociferous in acknowledging the debt which Greek geometry owed to the priests of Isis and Osiris. However, their effusive appraisal of the Egyptian contribution has not been borne out by the papyri deciphered in the course of the last century. Indeed, these documents reveal that Egyptian geometry, even when considered as an empirical effort, was so rudimentary, if not crude, that the Greeks could not have conceivably derived anything worth while from that source.

However, considerable progress has been recently made in deciphering the cuneiform inscriptions on the clay tablets discovered among the ruins of ancient Babylon. These studies have disclosed that the Babylonians possessed a much greater store of scientific knowledge than has hitherto been suspected. In *arithmetic*, for instance, they had devised a positional numeration and even a symbol equivalent to our decimal point; in *algebra*, they knew how to set up quadratic and cubic equations, and had even contrived to solve such equations by means of elaborate numerical tables; finally, in *geometry*, too, they had by far excelled the Egyptians in measuring areas and volumes. These archaeological studies have led some writers to conjecture that Babylonian learning had in some way infiltrated into Greece, say, during the sixth century or even before, which could account for the extraordinary progress of Greek mathematics in the ensuing centuries.

10

It is not my purpose here to examine this hypothesis in detail. After all, it matters little where the Greeks obtained the geometrical material on which they eventually erected their geometry. The issue is where, when and how *the method of deductive reasoning* emerged to turn geometry into a mathematical discipline. The "Babel" theory would acquire significance only if its proponents could establish that the Babylonians had arrived at their geometrical rules by means of deduction, and thus far the cuneiform inscriptions of the Babylonians have yielded no greater evidence to that effect than the hieroglyphics of the Egyptians.

There are several other questions which the supporters of the Babel hypothesis will have to answer before they can establish their theory on a sound footing. How is it that we find no mention of Babylonian influence in any of the accounts given by Greek commentators? If this was a deliberate and concerted attempt to conceal the sources of Greek erudition, why were the same men so generous in acknowledging their debt to the Egyptians? If the influence existed, why did it leave no trace in the field where the Chaldeans were most proficient and the Greeks most deficient, namely, in algebra? Certainly, in an age when the problems of doubling the cube and trisection were so much in vogue, the Babylonian methods of handling cubic equations could have been used with success.

II

I set out to trace the evolution of Greek geometry from its inception to the days when it had grown to full stature in the *Elements* of Euclid. This survey has revealed that the dominating motif of the first and last phases of that era was geometry as a discipline, while the stimulus of the intervening period was the challenge of the unsolved problems. The history of that era is like a symphony the finale of which is but a variation on the introductory theme, while the intermediate movements are built on quite a different motif, with the original theme as a mere accompaniment.

In a certain sense this survey was the defence of a thesis, and I fear that in spite of the arguments adduced in its support, the thesis will strike most of my readers as indefensible. Indeed, here is a comprehensive and well-integrated discipline which, having survived without appreciable change for more than two thousand years, remains today one of the bases of universal education. The idea that this achievement was the work of a single man, or even of a single generation, is so much at variance with accepted ideas on the progress of knowledge that it seems to border on the fantastic.

It does border on the fantastic, and in all fairness I must warn the reader that such fantasies await him at every twist and turn of mathematical history. I once attended a lecture of Poincaré during which he made the off-record remark that the history of mathematics resembles an anthology of amazing stories, and that geometry was the most amazing of the lot. So, I shall not attempt to strengthen my thesis with further argument, trusting that the reader who perseveres with me on these exotic excursions into the shadowland of number, form and extension will become immune to shocks and will finish by realizing that his original reaction has largely been due to preconceived notions on the progress of knowledge.

With this I rest my case.

45

Chapter Four

PYRAMIDS

It is not that history repeats itself, but that historians repeat each other.

D'ALEMBERT

I

We journey to the valley of Giza, one-time burial ground of the ancient Pharaohs. The huge tombs of these long-forgotten potentates still stand, enduring monuments to their colossal vainglory and to the technical prowess of an age which antedates Greek civilization by more than four thousand years. Among these structures, sprawling over more than twenty acres and rising to nearly five hundred feet above its base, looms the Pyramid of Cheops, surnamed the Great.

In this grandiose setting was taught, according to Greek legend, the first lesson in deductive geometry. The *time*: about 600 B.C. The *pupils*: the venerable priests of Isis and Osiris, a cult so old as to appear rooted in eternity. The *teacher*: one Thales, a Greek who had come to those shores with the express purpose of wresting from these very priests the secrets of their mystic knowledge. The *problem*: to determine the altitude of the Great Pyramid.

Why did the priests put the problem to Thales? Was it a challenge designed to put the upstart Greek in his place? Were they unable to solve the problem by their own efforts? Is it conceivable that a people who had displayed such skill in planning and erecting these elaborate structures could not handle a problem which would rate today as a routine exercise for a high-school sophomore?

The chroniclers of the tale offered no answers to these and similar questions. They confined themselves to the claim that Thales had solved the problem in a brilliant and rigorous fashion, by *measuring the shadow of the Pyramid at an hour when a man's shadow was equal to his height.*

2

The etymology of the word "pyramid" lends some authenticity to the preceding tale. The Greek *pyramis* was an adaptation of the Egyptian *pyremus* which, curiously enough, denoted neither an imperial tomb nor a geometrical solid. *Pyremus* was Egyptian for *altitude*. The word was probably frequently used in extolling the loftiness of these monuments, and this might have led the Greeks to identify the word with the edifice itself, and later with any solid which resembled such an edifice in form. Be this as it may, the term eventually acquired an even broader significance. For, while all Egyptian Pyramids have *square bases* and *congruent faces*, the term "pyramid," as defined by Euclid and as accepted by us today, applies to *any solid*, symmetric or otherwise, *with a polygonal base and triangular faces converging to a point.*

Now, we are concerned here not with the authenticity of this tale but rather with its plausibility, which is quite another matter. Indeed, it would be idle to speculate whether the Egyptians had actually propounded the problem to Thales, or whether he had solved the problem proposed. On the other hand, the answer to the following two questions would contribute materially to an appraisal of the status of mathematics of that period: First, was it within the ken of the Egyptian scholars of the period to determine the altitude of a pyramid? Second, could Thales have determined the altitude of the Great Pyramid by the method attributed to him, utilizing only such ideas as lay within his own ken?

3

Consider a symmetric pyramid with a square base, *PQRS*, such as is shown in Figure 1. Denote by *a* the side of the square; by *b* the slant height, i.e., the perpendicular dropped from the apex

A onto any one of the sides; by *h* the altitude of the pyramid. Both *a* and *b* can be measured directly, and will, therefore, be assumed given; the problem is to calculate *h*. We consider a vertical plane through the apex *A* of the pyramid and parallel

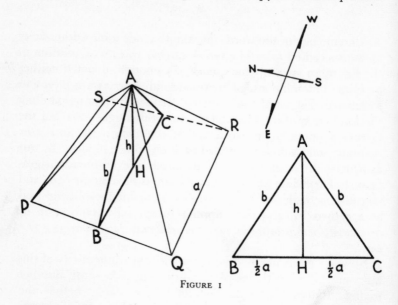

FIGURE I

to one of the sides of the base; it cuts the pyramid along the isosceles triangle *ABC*, the sides of which are *a*, *b* and *b* respectively, and the altitude of which, *AH*, is the quantity *h* sought. The application of the *hypotenuse theorem* to the right triangle *AHB* yields directly:

$$h = \sqrt{b^2 - (\tfrac{1}{2}a)^2}.$$

Still, however simple this approach may appear today, it lay beyond the mathematical ken of the period under consideration. To be sure, the Egyptians knew of isolated cases where the hypotenuse relation held, such as the "triples" (3, 4; 5) or (5, 12; 13), but there is no evidence whatever that they were aware of the general validity of the Pythagorean theorem. Furthermore, a practical application of the theorem

48

involves *rational approximations to quadratic surds*, a technique which, as far as we know, the Egyptians did not possess.

This does not mean that the Egyptians had no means at their disposal for calculating the altitude of the Great Pyramid. The form of a symmetric pyramid with square base depends only on the ratio $(k = h/a)$ of altitude to the side of the base, which, in turn, completely determines the dihedral angle between the base and any one of the faces. Now, it so happens that these data are sensibly the same for all the Pyramids of Giza, the angle varying between $50°$ and $52°$, and the ratio between $0 \cdot 63$ and $0 \cdot 64$, averaging about $7/11$. In other words, the Pyramids of Giza are very nearly *similar solids*, which means that if the ratio k were known for any one of the Pyramids, it could serve to calculate the altitude for any other. One of the smaller Pyramids the altitude of which was amenable to direct measurement could have been used to determine the ratio; or, and this is far more likely, a miniature model could have been built for the purpose at hand. And we must remember that the Egyptians were past masters of the miniature.

4

This near-similarity of Egyptian Pyramids has been the subject of much speculation in recent times. One could explain this uniformity by observing that the construction of this imposing array of tombs was spread over more than a thousand years, so that the builders of the later pyramids had before their eyes magnificent models consecrated by tradition. But then why was the first pyramid erected on such odd proportions? Why these unorthodox angles and ratios?

One plausible conjecture is that the choice was dictated by engineering considerations. The granite veneer of these tombs was laid upon massive masonry; to haul the bricks, mortar and stones up the steep slopes required the toil, tears, sweat and blood of an army of slaves. There was a limiting angle beyond which the expenditure in slave lives became uneconomical, for even the life of a slave had a price. Thus, the ratio *k* might have been a sort of "coefficient of human endurance," and 7/11 measured the limit of that endurance.

However, such a matter-of-fact account would hardly satisfy those who have a penchant toward the occult. Indeed, nothing short of a religious, or at least aesthetic, interpretation is acceptable: the proportion must have been a sacrament, a criterion of beauty, or both! But why should 7 and 11 be singled out for this unique mission? Is it because of the singular role these magic numbers play in the vicissitudes of a game of dice? This is one occult argument that has not yet been advanced to explain the peculiarities in the design of the Egyptian Pyramids; I hasten to add that some of the theories advanced are just about as reasonable.

Most popular among the aesthetes is the theory which associates the design of the Egyptian Pyramids—and every other design, human or divine—with the so-called *golden section*. I shall deal in detail with these pretensions in the next chapter. The propounders of another theory point out that 11/7 is an approximation to $\frac{1}{2}\pi$, i.e., to the ratio of the semicircumference of a circle to its diameter. They claim that the designers of the Pyramids had chosen this proportion because they viewed the semicircle as a figure unexcelled in beauty. However, studies of the hieroglyphic papyri have failed to reveal any such predilection.

5

"He determined the height of the Great Pyramid by measuring the shadow it cast at an hour when a man's shadow was equal to his height." In these words does the Greek historian Hieronymus describe the feat of the Wizard of Miletus. Other historians, classical and modern, too, reiterate this statement with some variations, but without critical comment. One is reminded of d'Alembert's *bon mot*: "It is not that history repeats itself, but that historians repeat each other."

It would be simple enough to reconstruct the alleged solution of Thales if the problem had been to determine the altitude of an obelisk, or of any solid whose horizontal dimensions were negligible as compared with the vertical; for, at the time of the day when the sunrays struck the ground at an angle of 45°, the shadow of the obelisk would be sensibly equal to the height, and such inaccuracy as would be introduced by the horizontal dimensions of the solid could be readily discounted. But the object was not an obelisk; it was a massive pyramid, the horizontal and vertical dimensions of which were of comparable magnitude.

The shadow of a pyramid is a triangle, and the shape of the triangle depends not only on the relative dimensions of the

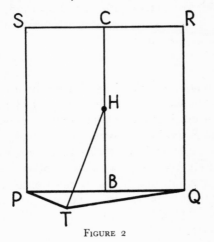

FIGURE 2

solid and on the hour of observation but on the latitude of the place and on the orientation of the sides. Now, the Egyptians were sun worshippers, and it was the obvious intention of the builders to orient the horizontal edges of these tombs East–West and South–North. In this they succeeded admirably. The angular deviation of the South–North edges from the true meridian, the so-called *azimuth*, nowhere exceeds one fourth of a degree; as a matter of fact, recent surveying has shown that the azimuth of the Great Pyramid is less than 4 minutes. Thus, for all intents and purposes, we may consider the edges of the Great Pyramid as oriented along the *cardinal* directions of the compass.

In Figure 2 the shadow triangle is *PQT*, and at the hour when the rays of the sun strike the ground at an angle of $45°$ the altitude of the pyramid and the line TH are equal. If PQT were an isosceles triangle, then to determine TH it would be sufficient to measure the perpendicular distance of the tip T to the edge PQ and add to it $\frac{1}{2}a$. However, the vertical plane which passes through the apex A perpendicular to the edge PQ is not parallel to the *ecliptic*, i.e., to the plane of the apparent path of the sun but is inclined to it at a substantial angle. The effect of this "obliquity" is that the triangle PQT is not isosceles, and this materially complicates the computation of the line TH which measures the altitude of the pyramid.

6

As a matter of fact, in order to determine the distance between the tip T of the shadow and the centre H of the base of the pyramid, it would be necessary not only to measure the sides of the triangle PQT but also to carry out calculations involving repeated application of the Pythagorean theorem, and culminating in the extraction of a square root, calculations which by far transcend the ken of the period under consideration. On the other hand, we cannot rule out the possibility that Thales turned the difficulty by some artifice based on the *principle of similitude*.

One such artifice is shown in Figure 3. Let HA and ha indicate two vertical posts, and HT and ht their shadows at some given time; *these shadows are proportional to the altitudes* of the posts. Suppose next that at another time of the day the respective shadows of the two posts are HT' and ht'; these, too, are proportional to the altitudes. It follows that $t't : th = T'T : TH$. In particular, if $t't = th$, then $T'T = TH$.

Returning now to the situation which allegedly confronted Thales, let ha designate the position of the man whom he was observing, and let ht be the shadow of the man at the time of the afternoon when one's shadow equals one's height; finally, let T be the tip of the shadow cast by the Pyramid at that time. Thales marks the points T and t, and with t as centre.

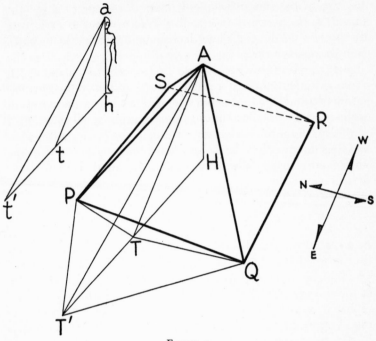

FIGURE 3

draws the circle which passes through *h*. He then waits; as the shadows lengthen, there comes a time when the tip of the man's shadow strikes the circle drawn, say in *t'*. Simultaneously, the tip of the Pyramid's shadow has moved from *T* to *T'*, and $TT' = TH = HA$, because $tt' = th = ha$. Thus the altitude of the point *A* above the plane of the base is determined by the horizontal line *TT'*, which is fully accessible to direct measurement.

7

This conjectured solution depends neither on the latitude of the place, nor on the obliquity of the ecliptic, nor, for that matter, on the form of the solid. It would obviously apply to determining the altitude of any point *A*, provided *two consecutive positions of its shadow* *T* and *T'* were known. Besides, it has

53

the merit of presupposing only such ideas and methods as existed at the time when the incident is alleged to have occurred. In short, what the conjecture lacks in authenticity, it makes up in *historical plausibility*.

Indeed, the conjecture would be plausible even if the episode had taken place at a much earlier age, since the *conception of similitude* antedates deductive geometry by thousands of years. For, not only is similitude a prerequisite to all geometrical thinking, but it dominates the graphic arts as well, and the fact that these arts have been cultivated since time immemorial shows how deeply the conception is rooted in man's consciousness.

Chapter Five

PENTACLES

I shall indulge my sacred fury . . . .
JOHANNES KEPLER

I

In one of the *Dialogues*, Plato puts into the mouth of Timaeus, a follower of Pythagoras, the following words: "It is impossible to join two things in a beautiful manner without a third being present, for a bond must exist to unite them, and this is best achieved by a proportion. For, if of three magnitudes the mean is to the least as the greatest to the mean, and, conversely, the least is to the mean as the mean to the greatest—then is the last the first and the mean, and the mean the first and the last. Thus are all by necessity the same, and since they are the same, they are but one."

The problem to which this exotic verbiage alludes has come to be known as *golden section*, or division of a magnitude into *extreme and mean reason*, the word *"reason"* being used here in the archaic sense of *ratio*. Translated into mathematical language the problem is to divide a given magnitude, say a rectilinear segment of length s, into two parts, such that the greater, x, be to the whole as the lesser part is to the greater. Hence the proportion:

$$x : s = (s - x) : x. \qquad \qquad (5.1)$$

This, in turn, leads to the quadratic equation,

$$x^2 + sx - s^2 = 0, \qquad \qquad (5.2)$$

the *positive root* of which is

$$x = \tfrac{1}{2}s(\sqrt{5} - 1). \qquad \qquad (5.3)$$

55

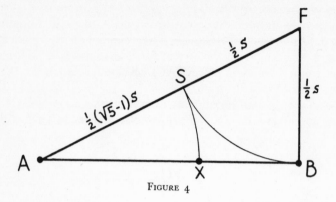

FIGURE 4

A simple straightedge-compass construction, based on a direct interpretation of this last formula, is shown in Figure 4. In the right triangle ABF we have by construction: $AB = s$, $SF = \frac{1}{2}s = BF$ and $AX = AS$. Hence:

$$AX = \tfrac{1}{2}s\sqrt{5} - \tfrac{1}{2}s = \tfrac{1}{2}s(\sqrt{5} - 1) = x$$

i.e., the point X divides the given segment AB in the ratio sought.

2

In the Dark and Middle Ages, the golden section became a favourite topic of theological speculation. Many a Schoolman, inspired by the arguments of the Pythagoreans and Platonists, sought and found in the proportion a key to the mystery of creation, declaring that extreme and mean reason was the very principle which the Supreme Architect had adopted in cosmic and global design: hence, the title *"divine proportion"* bestowed upon the ratio. Nor were these mystic meditations the monopoly of medieval monks. The virus affected quite a few poets and painters of the Renaissance, including Leonardo da Vinci himself. Of this, however, later.

The modern revival of the golden-section cult, like so many other movements of the kind, is characterized by what may be called "rationalizing the occult." Its devotees, mostly artists, accentuate the aesthetic value of the proportion, its prevalence in nature, the exhaustive role it plays in human anatomy, its cosmic significance. They claim that the golden section is the clue to the beauty of Greek sculpture, as well as to the finest specimens of antique architecture such as the Egyptian Pyramids.

One of these claims is illustrated in Figure 5. The sides of the rectangle are in "divine proportion." The pattern will

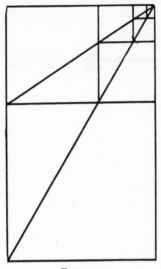

FIGURE 5

strike the reader as quite familiar, since many objects in our immediate environment have this particular design: windows, tables, books, boxes, playing cards. We are assured by golden-section enthusiasts that this pattern is the incarnation of grace, and that it is recognized by most people as such. Are these contentions supported by facts? Well, as far back as 1876, the German psychologist, Gustav Theodor Fechner, spurred on perhaps by the golden sectionists of his day, conducted a series of experiments on a large and heterogeneous group of people. Ten rectangular patterns ranging in form from 2 by 5 to 1 by 1, and including the golden section, were placed at random in a room, and the individuals were requested to record as to which of these shapes appeared to them as the most graceful. While the golden section received more votes than any other, it appealed only to one third of those interviewed. On the whole, the results were rather inconclusive.

Among the attempts at accounting for this alleged preference on rational grounds is the contention that when the human eye surveys a rectangular pattern, it instinctively separates from it a *square*. (Figure 5.) Ostensibly, the closer the remainder resembles the whole, the more the pattern appeals to the eye. The ideal, of course, is provided by the *golden-section* rectangle, inasmuch as here *the residual rectangle is similar to the original*. Such endeavours to trace one doubtful predilection to another just as doubtful are characteristic of the specious reasoning of the aesthete.

3

In appraising the validity of these claims, one should bear in mind that the golden-section "ratio" is an *irrational number*. Indeed, setting in equation (5.2) $x/s = D$, we find

$$D^2 + D - 1 = 0, \qquad \cdot \qquad \cdot \qquad (5.4)$$

the positive root of which is

$$D = \tfrac{1}{2}(\sqrt{5} - 1). \qquad \cdot \qquad \cdot \qquad (5.5)$$

The numerical value of D with five correct decimal places is 0·61803. To vindicate their claims that the golden section is the motive of such and such a design, human or divine, the golden sectionist will seek to prove that the measured value agrees with the one calculated, within "reasonable limits," of course. Obviously, the success of his undertaking will depend on the latitude allowed in interpreting the term "reasonable limits."

A case in point is the allegation that the designers of the Egyptian tombs had been guided by the *golden-section* rule. As mentioned in the preceding chapter, the ratio of altitude to side has an average value of 0·625, and never falls below

0·63 for any of the Pyramids of Giza. The mean discrepancy between this ratio and the extreme and mean reason is more than $2\frac{1}{2}$ per cent., and such a difference could hardly be ignored without stretching reason to the extreme.

Just as specious are the contentions that certain proportions in human anatomy conform to the *golden-section* rule, as for example that the navel divides the average man's height in extreme and mean reason. Even if such biometrical data could be established, how could one reconcile them with the aesthetic claims mentioned above? For, surely, even the most ardent golden sectionist would hardly contend that the average human stature embodied his idea of grace.

Now, given the privilege of selecting the traits to be compared, the freedom of choosing and grouping the specimens which are to be measured for these traits and a latitude in the degree of precision allowed in interpreting the data measured— with all these liberties at one's disposal, one should be able to turn any recondite mystery into a mathematical law, and, as a matter of fact, into a law assigned in advance. This sounds like accentuating the obvious, and so it is. But, evidently, it is not so obvious to the authors of some of the studies, biometric, econometric, psychometric, which have come to my notice.

4

While on the subject of *rational approximations to irrational magnitudes*, I must mention one striking property of the extreme and mean reason which could have furnished much grist to the occult mill of the golden sectionists, if the medium in which this property is expressed lay within the ken of the cult; I am speaking of the expansion of the irrational $\frac{1}{2}(\sqrt{5} - 1)$ into a *continued fraction.**

I shall have much to say about this important device later. For the purpose at hand it is best to approach the matter from the *heuristic* point of view. We have by definition

$$D : 1 = 1 : (1 + D).$$

* See Chapter 12.

Accordingly, we can write

$$D = \frac{1}{1 + D} = \frac{1}{1 + \dfrac{1}{1 + D}} = \text{etc.} \ldots ,$$

from which we infer that the golden-section ratio is the *limit of the infinite continued fraction*

$$D = \tfrac{1}{2}(\sqrt{5} - 1) = \cfrac{1}{1 + \cfrac{1}{1 + \cfrac{1}{1 + \ldots}}} \qquad . \quad (5.6)$$

the most simple of its kind, since not only are all the denominators equal, but their common value is *one*.

To the mystic, the mere circumstance that an entity can be expressed by a single symbol is portentous enough; but when that one symbol is *one*, then the divine origin of the entity transcends all doubt. For, *one* is the emblem of God; in the words of the mystic Leibnitz: "One has sufficed to draw all out of nought." That it would require an infinitude of steps to attain the desired goal lends power to the interpretation, inasmuch as the infinite, too, is an attribute of the Deity. Finally, there is an *absolute quality* to a continued fraction which no other representation possesses: *it is independent of the scale of numeration*. Thus, the "spectrum" would have been the same had Providence chosen to equip man with 12, or 60, or any number of fingers in lieu of the random 10. This disquisition is offered here for what it is worth as this author's humble contribution to the cult of the occult.

5

A favourite method of exhibiting the alleged role played by the golden section in human anatomy is shown in Figure 6. The picture is taken from a modern book on the subject, but the scheme of presenting the posture of a man as a five-pointed figure can be traced to Leonardo da Vinci and his mathe-

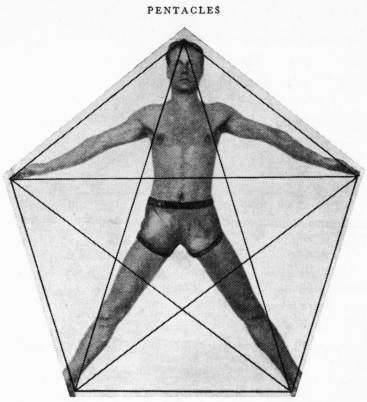

FIGURE 6

matical collaborator, the monk Luca Pacioli. The latter's book, entitled *Divine Proportion*, contained a number of striking drawings by da Vinci, two of which are reproduced in Figure 9. The tract was published in 1509, and many of the ideas propounded by the modern devotees of the cult hark back to that period.

The point of departure of these occult speculations is an isosceles triangle with angles 36°, 72° and 72° (*ABC* in Figure 7). In such a "golden-section triangle," the angular bisector, *AD*, determines two *isosceles triangles, DAB* and *DAC,* and the latter is *similar to the original triangle.* From this follows: *first,* that the point *D* divides the side *BC in extreme and mean reason;* and *second,* that *the sides of a golden-section triangle are in divine proportion.*

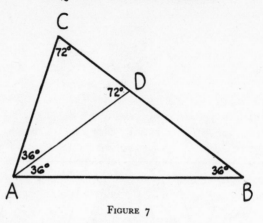

The configurations affected by these lemmas are:

(*a*) The *regular pentagon*. (Figure 8a.) Here, *ACD* is a golden-section triangle; hence, *the side and diagonal of a regular pentagon are in divine proportion.*

(*b*) The *regular pentagram*. (Figure 8b.) Here *ABC* is a golden-section triangle. It follows that *the sides of a regular pentagram divide one another in golden section.*

(*c*) The *regular decagon*. (Figure 8c.) Here *AOB* is a golden-section triangle; hence, *the side of a regular decagon and the radius of the circumscribed circle are in divine proportion.*

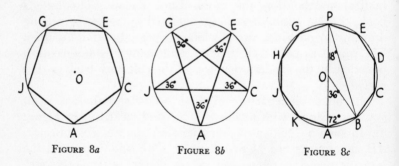

FIGURE 8*a*   FIGURE 8*b*   FIGURE 8*c*

6

While the origin of the golden-section idea is obscure, it is quite probable that the Pythagoreans were led to endow the ratio with occult significance because of the property of the pentagram described above, namely, that its sides divide one another in extreme and mean reason. We know that the pentagram had played an important role in the ritual of many ancient people, that it was a sacred symbol of the Pythagorean Order, and that to this day some "secret" societies which hail Pythagoras as their spiritual forebear use this mystic figure as talisman.

The effect of Christianity on popular fancy was to turn the sacred into the occult. The pentagram of the Greeks became *pentacle*, indispensable item of the sorcerer's gear. In some places the mark of the pentacle was a tiding of evil; in others, on the contrary, it was viewed as a sure deterrent against Satan's machinations. In some languages it was called *devil's hoof*, in others *witch's foot*. In the course of time, the geometrical origin of the term was all but forgotten, until *pentacle* became a symbol of black magic and the conjuror's art.

Several theories have been advanced to explain this strange predilection. One of these traces the preference to the five fingers of the human hand, maintaining that the occult powers ascribed to the pentagram did not derive from its geometrical properties, but from its association with the number *five*. It may be pointed out in this connection that the Platonists attached as much importance to the pentagon as to the pentagram, and that the number five was an important adjunct to their cosmic speculations.

7

This brings me to another corner of that occult fringe which surrounds the early history of geometry.

Consider first a regular convex polygon of n sides. The n vertices of the figure lie on a circle, and there exists another circle which is tangent to all *n* sides. Thus the construction of a regular *n*-gon is fully equivalent to the division of the circumference of a circle into *n* equal arcs, a problem known as *cyclotomy*. The problem admits of a solution for any value of the integer *n*, and however involved may be the actual construction of the corresponding *n*-gon, the difficulty is technical in nature and not a matter of principle.

When we pass from the plane to space, we find the situation quite different. In lieu of polygons we have here *polyhedra*, i.e., solids bounded by planes. The boundary planes of a polyhedron intersect in lines which are called *edges*; the edges, in turn, converge in the *vertices* of the solid and combine into polygons which are called the *faces* of the polyhedron. Denote the number of faces, edges and vertices of any given polyhedron by *f*, *e* and *v* respectively: these integers are connected by certain relations known as *Euler equations*.

When we say that a polyhedron is *convex* we mean that the solid lies *on one side of any one of its faces*; when we say that the polyhedron is *regular*, we mean that its faces are *congruent regular polygons*. When both of these conditions are met, then the vertices of the solid lie on a sphere and there exists another sphere which touches all the faces of the solid. Let *n* be the number of sides in any face, and *m* the number of edges which emerge from any vertex: then the Euler equations mentioned above reduce to

$$f + v = e + 2$$
$$nf = mv = 2e. \qquad\qquad (5 \cdot 7)$$

Five solutions of these equations are given in the table below, and it is not difficult to show that *no others exist*.

Solid	f	v	e	m	n	Face
Tetrahedron . .	4	4	6	3	3	Triangle
Hexahedron (Cube)	6	8	12	3	4	Square
Octahedron . .	8	6	12	4	3	Triangle
Dodecahedron .	12	20	30	3	5	Pentagon
Icosahedron . .	20	12	30	5	3	Triangle

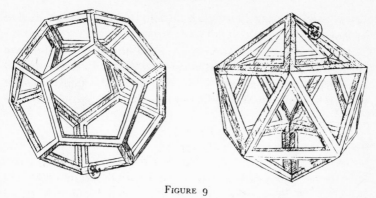

FIGURE 9

Two of these polyhedra are shown in Figure 9. They are taken from the *Divine Proportion* of Pacioli, who attributed the drawings to Leonardo da Vinci. The choice was obviously motivated by the fact that both solids contain *regular pentagons*, the *dodecahedron* being distinguished by its *pentagonal* faces, while the five triangles which emanate from a vertex of the *icosahedron* form a pyramid with *pentagonal* base.

8

The discovery of the regular polyhedra has been ascribed to Plato; hence the name of *"Platonic solids"* under which these bodies are commonly known. That Plato was their discoverer may be seriously doubted, but the knowledge that there were five such solids, and only five, must have been very gratifying to him and his disciples. However, this posed a new problem: cosmic harmony demanded a one-to-one correspondence between these perfect solids and the basic constituents of matter, and Platonic cosmogony recognized only *four* such *primordial elements*: *earth, fire, water* and *air*.

The vexing problem was eventually solved by invoking a principle which has governed occult speculations since time immemorial: "When in doubt, let the Deity have the hindmost!" One of the perfect solids must be assigned to the heavens! But which? The most perfect, of course: the *dodeca-*

hedron, whose *pentagonal* faces bore the imprint of the perfect proportion.

And so it was that having assigned the cube to the firm earth, and having conferred a solid each on the more ephemerous fire, water and air, Plato dedicated the dodecahedron with its sacred pentagonal faces to the heavens.

9

I shall now quote from a letter written two thousand odd years later: ". . . Before the universe was created, there were no numbers except the Trinity which is God himself . . . For, the line and the plane imply no numbers: here infinitude itself reigns. Let us consider, therefore, the solids. We must first eliminate the irregular solids, because we are concerned here only with orderly creation. There remain six bodies, the sphere and the five regular polyhedra. To the sphere corresponds the outer heaven. For, the universe is twofold: dynamic and static. The static is the image of God-Essence, while the dynamic is but the image of God-Creator, and is therefore of a lower order. In its very nature, the round corresponds to God and the flat to his creation. Indeed, the sphere is threefold: surface, centre, volume; so is the static world: firmament, sun, ether; and so is God: Son, Father, Spirit. On the other hand, the dynamic world is represented by the flat-faced solids. Of these there are five; when viewed as boundaries, however, these five determine six distinct things; hence, the six planets that revolve about the sun. This is also the reason why there are but six planets. And because the sun stands at the centre of creation, and because it is at rest and yet the source of all motion, it is the true image of God, the Father, the Creator. For, what God is to creation, is motion to the sun . . ."

". . . I have further shown that the regular solids fall into two groups: three in one, and two in the other. To the larger group belongs, first of all, the Cube, then the Pyramid, and finally the Dodecahedron. To the second group belongs, first, the Octahedron, and, second, the Icosahedron. That is why the most important portion of the universe, the Earth—

where God's image is reflected in man—separates the two groups. For, as I have proved next, the solids of the first group must lie beyond the earth's orbit, and those of the second group within. . . . Thus was I led to assign the CUBE to SATURN, the TETRAHEDRON to JUPITER, the DODECAHEDRON to MARS, the ICOSAHEDRON to VENUS, and the OCTAHEDRON to MERCURY. . . .

Does this sound to you like the raving of a maniac, or a page out of Madame Blavatzky? Then be reassured; these are excerpts from Johannes Kepler's own preview of a tract which he published in 1596 under the title *The Cosmic Mystery*. And such was the spirit of that period that when the essay reached Galileo and Tycho Brahe, both astronomers responded with flattering comments. As a matter of fact, the latter was so impressed that he invited young Kepler to become his assistant, urging him at the same time to apply his mystic methods to the Tychonian cosmic system which was sort of a cross between the Ptolemaic and the Copernican, the planets spinning around the Sun, while the latter was executing an exotic pirouette about the Earth.

10

Kepler called his correspondence between planets and polyhedra *Mysterium Cosmographicum*. That he regarded it not as mere rhetorics but as a pictorial presentation of an actual mathematical relation which governed the solar system is attested by the sketch reproduced in Figure 10. To be sure, the projected model never did get beyond the drawing stage; not, however, because Kepler had lost faith in his youthful conception, but because he could not raise the funds for its construction.

Now, there is nothing loose or even indeterminate in the mathematics of the scheme; if anything, it is too rigid. Indeed, if we assume, as Kepler did, that *the planetary orbits are concentric and coplanar circles with the sun in the centre of the system,*

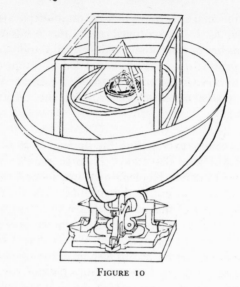

FIGURE 10

then the first step is to determine the relative magnitudes of the radii of these circles. Denote these radii by the initial letters in the names of the six planets, s, j, m, e, v and m'; and let S, J, M, E, V, M' designate the *six spheres* which admit these orbits for great circles. Then, according to Kepler, there exists a cube the vertices of which rest on the sphere S, and the faces of which are tangent to the sphere J. Since the diagonal of that cube is the diameter of S, and its side the diameter of J, it follows that s is to j as *the diagonal of a cube is to its side*, i.e., $s/j = \sqrt{3}$. By similar geometrical considerations one can derive the ratios m/j, e/m, etc., culminating in a set of proportions: a complete arithmetic counterpart of the *Mysterium Cosmographicum*.

The question is to what extent do these results agree with the subsequent observations of Kepler and with the laws which he deduced from these observations? Now, the first of these laws declares that the planetary orbits are *not circles but ellipses with the sun as common focus*; well, the *eccentricities* of these orbits are so small that they could readily be taken for circles as a first approximation. The second law declares that the motion of a planet is such that *equal sectors are covered in equal intervals of time*, while the third states that *the square of the period* consumed in a complete revolution is proportional to *the cube of the major axis* of the planet's orbit. Both the second and the third law hold for circular orbits. Thus, with certain reasonable reservations, the *Mysterium* could be accepted as the model of the solar system, *provided that the proportions of which I spoke above were in agreement with astronomical data.*

The puzzling fact, however, is that these proportions do not even remotely agree with those derived from observations. Thus we found $s/j = \sqrt{3} = 1 \cdot 732$, whereas the ratio of the mean distances to the sun of Saturn and Jupiter is $1 \cdot 833 \ldots$ The error, of nearly 6 per cent., is of a size that cannot be taken lightly, and the discrepancy between observed and calculated values is even greater for the remaining proportions. It has been argued that the *Mysterium* was designed before Kepler got access to Tycho Brahe's observations, and this is certainly true. Still, Kepler never did retract his early work; on the contrary, a quarter of a century later, in a book entitled *De Harmonici Mundi*, he amplified the *Mysterium* by endowing it with sound: under the impact of the moving orbs, the invisible spheres emitted tones of varying intensity but of pitch so high that only the sentient soul of God, who dwelt in the sun, could perceive this *music of the spheres*.

II

There has been a tendency on the part of some of Kepler's biographers to palliate his occult activities and to portray the man as a detached observer bent on ascertaining the truth no matter how sharply this truth contradicted his own preconceptions. These interpreters point out that Kepler's title of Imperial Astronomer carried more honour than honorarium; that even this scant pay was perennially in arrear, so much so that upon his death the exchequer still owed him 20,000 florins; that to supplement this meagre income Kepler had to resort to reading horoscopes, which, allegedly, explains his extensive excursions into astrology. As to his mystic speculations on the nature of the *cosmos*, these interpreters hint that

Kepler had uttered them with tongue in cheek, largely as a concession to the spirit of his time, or, at worst, as a means to impress the half-educated men on whom his advancement depended.

Now, unlike the mystic philosophers of classical Greece, Kepler left behind a wealth of autobiographical material. This *Kepleriana* suggests to my mind not the portrait of a learned opportunist but that of a mystic obsessed with the conviction that he had been chosen by Providence to reveal to man the essential unity between the motions of heavenly bodies, the harmony of sound, the logic of number and the beauty of geometrical form. It was this conviction, this "sacred fury" as he called it, that impelled him, in my opinion, to pursue, throughout life and to the end, the cosmic phantom which he had conceived in his youth. He wrote: "Nothing shall stop me. I shall indulge my sacred fury. I shall triumph over mankind. I have stolen the golden vases of the Egyptians to erect a tabernacle to my God. . . . The die is cast, the book is written to be read now or later, I care not which. It may well wait a century for a reader: has not God waited for an observer these six thousand years?"

Was he referring to his laws of planetary motion or to his *Mysterium Cosmographicum*? Well, as far as we know he made no such distinction. Both were parts of the sacred tabernacle, and I am quite sure that, faced with the choice, he would have put the *Mysterium* first.

No, the arguments of the apologists notwithstanding, I, for one, cannot escape the conclusion that it was while endeavouring to substantiate his occult illusions that he had discovered the laws without which Newton could not have, in turn, discovered the principle of universal gravitation.

12

What could impel men of unquestioned scientific competence and integrity to carry out protracted and painstaking observations, subject these data to a keen and thorough mathematical treatment, and at the same time profess to see in their work the confirmation of some phantastic code which they have imposed on God or Nature? I have no answer to this question, but I have lived long enough to know that this schizophrenia, so manifest in Kepler, is far more prevalent among men of science than is commonly believed.

The occult has had many facets, and not all of these were of the naïve variety described in this chapter. In mathematics, the occult never outgrew these cruder forms, and that may be the reason why here it remained on the fringes of the science. In some fields contiguous to mathematics the occult has assumed more subtle and hence less recognizable forms. Indeed, listening to some modern physical theories one is often at a loss to understand wherein these exotic speculations differ from the mystic introspections of a Pythagoras or a Kepler.

The occult was not born with Pythagoras, nor has it died with Kepler. The historian looks back and beholds that much of the sacred of a yesteryear is condemned today as occult, and he wonders what will become of our discarded axioms.

Chapter Six

THE PSEUDOMATH

. . . such folly, unfortunately, is never confined to one subject, since the habit of fallacious thinking, even as that of correct reasoning, has a tendency to increase.

CONDORCET

I

Among the imposing array of problems which have graced mathematics during its long and eventful history there is a small group which has exerted a peculiar fascination on the amateur. To this group belong the famous problems of construction on which I touched in earlier chapters; here also belongs the Euclidean postulate of parallels. Several other problems may be listed under this head; of these, I shall mention only the Fermat problem: to demonstrate that the equation $x^n + y^n = z^n$ has no solutions in whole numbers as long as n itself is an integer greater than 2.

While the difficulties inherent in these problems can only be met by the resources of modern algebra and analysis, their preliminary formulation requires neither the exotic symbolism nor the weird terminology which obscure to the layman so many mathematical questions. Thus, whether the issue is construction or proof, the aims of these problems appear clear cut and direct, even to those who possess little mathematical training or insight. This tantalizing simplicity has deceived many an amateur, with the result that no end of "solutions" appeared, one as pretentious and as preposterous as the other.

While the amateur receives but little encouragement from the orthodox mathematician—a circumstance which he promptly attributes to professional jealousy—he finds the newspaper editor quite receptive, as a rule. In fact, some papers have regarded such achievements of sufficient importance as to be

72

featured as front-page news; others even have gone so far as to herald in glaring headlines that such or such an age-old problem, which has defied the efforts of countless generations of professional mathematicians, has in this day and age been completely solved by a nonprofessional. In this manner the amateur may gain considerable notoriety; unfortunately, his glory is soon eclipsed when a competing amateur with a conflicting solution of the same age-old problem manages to gain the ear of another equally credulous editor. It is by dint of such publicity that the "famous" problems are daily gaining in fame to the amusement of the expert and the confusion of the public.

2

These problems have played a considerable role in the history of mathematics. Not that they were key problems, in the sense that without their exhaustive solutions the disciplines in which they had arisen could not have progressed. No, their role can best be compared to that of a catalytic agent which precipitates chemical action without participating in it. Thus, these problems have been responsible for the invention of many a new method, and, more often than not, whole new disciplines have followed in their wake. As in the parable of the vineyard, the heirs had failed to unearth the gold after laboriously plowing up the estate; yet, the loosened soil yielded a harvest which exceeded in wealth the anticipated treasure.

The ancient problems of trisection of an angle and duplication of a cube have in modern times led to the theory of equations and have been indirectly responsible for the introduction of the exceedingly important concept of *group*. The attempts to square the circle led to the discovery of *transcendentals*; the efforts to prove Fermat's theorem resulted in the theory of *ideals*; the failures to demonstrate the postulate of parallels culminated in the discovery of the *non-Euclidean* geometries, without which the theory of *relativity* would be unthinkable.

Of all these developments the ambitious amateur is, of course, wholly unaware. Indeed, he is, as a rule, not interested in developments which require the study of the work of others. Sufficient unto him is to know that the problem which he tackles has not yet been solved, or that it has been declared impossible by professional mathematicians. For the rest, he trusts in God and in his own powers or prowess.

3

It has fallen to my lot to come in contact with many of these individuals. I say this in no spirit of complaint, for whatever inconvenience or irritation they may have caused me has been amply rewarded by the experience which I gained while studying their unusual turn of mind. Indeed, I hoped at one time to use the accumulated material in an essay *on the pathology of human reasoning.* As years go by, however, it is becoming increasingly doubtful that I shall ever have the leisure to engage in such a project. Accordingly, I decided to present some of the material here.

While the mental kinks of these individuals are to mathematicians little more than objects of passing curiosity, the same should not be true of psychiatrists, more particularly of those who specialize in the study of megalomania. Indeed, I cherish the hope that among my readers there may be some such specialist who, stimulated by these casual remarks, will undertake a scientific investigation in this field which, to my knowledge, has not even been touched by the alienist.

4

It will be convenient to designate this specimen of humanity by a special name. The term "circle-squarer" is obviously misleading, for rarely do these individuals confine their efforts to this one classical problem. More often than not, they will regard any mathematical problem—or any problem, for that matter—as particularly adapted to their talents, provided the experts have failed to solve it or have reached negative results in its regard.

I propose to call these persons *pseudomaths*, a term coined by Augustus De Morgan. A substantial portion of his *Budget of Paradoxes* was devoted to the study of these individuals and their fallacies. Of the obsession with which the species is afflicted De Morgan had this to say: "The pseudomath is a person who handles mathematics as the monkey handled the razor. The creature tried to shave himself, as he had seen his master do; but not having any notion of the angle at which the razor was to be held, he cut his own throat. He never tried again, poor animal! But the pseudomath keeps to his work, proclaims himself cleanshaved, and all the rest of the world hairy. . . . The feeling which tempts him to these problems is that which, in romance, made it impossible for a knight to pass a castle which belonged to a giant or an enchanter. This rinderpest of geometry cannot be cured when once it has seated itself in the system. All that can be done is to apply what the learned call prophylactics to those who are yet sound. When once the virus gets into the brain, the victim goes round the flame like a moth—first one way and then the other, beginning again where he ended, and ending where he began."

5

They come from all strata of society and all walks of life. While the male of the species predominates, ladies, too, have entered the race. In fact, I have noticed of late that the number of feminine pseudomaths is on the increase which, perhaps, is but a symptom of the gradual emancipation of the fair sex. Most countries, races, creeds, professions and crafts are represented; my own list includes farmers and army officers; bankers, brokers and merchants; realtors and prospectors; doctors, dentists and lawyers; engineers, artists and artisans; teachers, preachers and even a college president.

How large is their number is a question that cannot be answered with any degree of accuracy. There are no societies of pseudomaths, which is not surprising, since every pseudomath, being in sole possession of the eternal truth, views every other as an impostor and a fraud. In the absence of such rosters, any estimate is but a guess; my own, based on personal contacts and correspondence, is that in this country alone their number must run into many thousands.

In spite of the fact that they are being recruited from so many different occupations and classes, they exhibit a remarkable similarity in their methods of approach to a problem as well as in the strategy they use to obtain recognition. When given an opportunity to defend their contentions, every one of the pseudomaths who has come under my observation used the same tactics, which may be best qualified as a policy of attrition. With tiresome laboriousness and endless detail he would demonstrate the obvious steps in his reasoning; but, arrived at the critical point, he would pass over it with the utmost speed. Indeed, I have found in my dealings with them that I can save myself a great deal of ennui by just listening listlessly and without the slightest interruption to their drone, patiently awaiting the imminent slur.

The variety of their interests is unbelievably great. Thus, the announcement in 1907 of the Wolfskehl prize for the first solution of the Fermat problem found such a tremendous response from the pseudomaths of the world that the handling of the correspondence became a gigantic task. The advent of the theory of relativity has deviated the efforts of many into this new channel, with the result that every so often we are graced with a new refutation of Einstein. Quite often I receive letters from some individual who has discovered a kinship between phenomena which to the benighted scientist appear worlds apart, while one possessed by a truly universal spirit has succeeded in uniting into a single synthesis the Euclidean postulate of parallels and the quadrature of the circle, the Fermat problem and perpetual motion, the principle of relativity and the existence of the Deity, the quantum theory of the atom, forecasts of the stock market, the abolition of wars, the solution of the econonic depression and the liberation of mankind from the Bolshevist scourge—to mention but a few of the achievements he claims.

6

Their dogged perseverance defies all description. They seem to thrive on abuse, discouragement and ridicule. They speak of their undying devotion to truth. It must be conceded that no pseudomath has ever derived material benefit from his discoveries, while most of them continually sacrifice wealth and position in their efforts to gain recognition. I do not believe that they are actuated by greed; in fact, I have a lurking suspicion that even those pseudomaths who have tried for the Wolfskehl prize of 100,000 marks were motivated more by the desire to justify in the eyes of their kin and friends their fruitless efforts of many years than by any hope of winning the prize.

To my mind the dominating motive which sustains them in the face of all failures is an inordinate craving for publicity. To attain this end they will stop before no humiliation. One of the most remarkable instances of this kind is the case of one James Smith, a merchant of Liverpool, who flourished in the sixties of the last century. Smith spent half of his life and a considerable fortune in defending his method of squaring the circle, a method which, with all irrelevancies removed, amounted to the declaration that the ratio of the circumference to the diameter of a circle was equal to exactly 25/8. He engaged in a voluminous correspondence with the leading British mathematicians of his time, among whom were such outstanding men as William Rowan Hamilton, Stokes, Clifford, and De Morgan. They all began by trying to set him right; they all ended by giving it up as a bad job. Some of the replies of these men were so devastating that any sane man would have immediately destroyed them for fear that they might see the light of day. Not James Smith! At a price to himself that must have amounted to a small fortune, he published the whole correspondence and distributed the book free of charge to friend and foe alike. This volume of five-hundred-odd pages is a human document of inestimable value to a psychopathologist.

7

There is a term used in physics to designate an effect which persists after the generating cause has ceased to act, such, for instance, as occurs in elastic or magnetic phenomena. Such a residual after-effect is known as *hysteresis* and could be aptly applied to many phenomena in the history of science, and of culture more generally.

The pseudomath is a case in point. Far from being a phenomenon peculiar to our own times, he is as old as mathematics and, in a certain sense, even older. Indeed, just as astronomy was preceded by astrology, and chemistry by alchemy, so was mathematics preceded by *pseudomathematics*. Thus, in the *prelogical* period of mathematics, all its adepts were pseudomaths, more or less. The deductive method has put an end to the usefulness of the pseudomath, yet he shall long persist as a sort of hysteresis.

That this specimen was already a problem in ancient Greece, even as far back as the days of Pericles, may be judged from a scene which occurs in Aristophanes' comedy *The Birds*. Meton, an Athenian surveyor—and a pseudomath if there ever was one—demands admission to the Bird State. When requested to give his qualifications, he offers to parcel off the atmosphere into acres, and to square the circle by means of a straightedge. He is refused admittance and asked to move on. He insists on knowing why, whereupon the following conversation takes place: "What danger is there? Is discord raging here?" "No, not at all!" "What is the matter then?" "In perfect concord are we resolved to kick out every humbug." It is interesting to note that twenty-four hundred years ago Aristophanes had a proper appreciation of such amateurish efforts, whereas editors of some of our modern dailies rarely miss a chance to blazon forth to the world that on such and such a date such and such a nonprofessional has at last solved a problem which has baffled professional mathematicians for nearly three thousand years.

The Dark Ages may be viewed as a sort of resurrection of the prelogical period. What little science was cultivated then was so hopelessly mixed up with pseudoscientific ideas that the task of a modern historian who deals with that period may well be compared with that of unscrambling an omelet. Mathematics was no exception: the *famous problems* were approached in the same spirit as the search for the philosopher's stone, or for the elixir of life. In fact, it was held by many that the quadrature of the circle would open the door to many such mysteries. Some of the most absurd solutions of the *famous problems* date from that period; furthermore, most of the fallacies of the modern pseudomath may be found in medieval literature. That there is little new under the sun applies to fallacies even more than it does to truth.

8

With the advent of modern times, there was an unprecedented increase in pseudomathematical activity. During the eighteenth century all scientific academies of Europe saw themselves besieged by circle-squarers, trisectors, duplicators and *perpetuum mobile* designers, loudly clamouring for recognition of their epoch-making achievements. In the second half of that century the nuisance had become so unbearable that, one by one, the academies were forced to discontinue the examination of the proposed solutions. The first to inaugurate this policy was the French Academy. To its published resolution there was attached an explanatory note written by the great Condorcet. The following are excerpts from this interesting document:

"The Academy has resolved this year not to examine in the future any solution of the problems of the doubling of the cube, the trisection of the angle and the squaring of the circle, or of any machine which lays claim to perpetual motion. . . . We have thought it to be our duty to account for the reasons which have led the Academy to adopt this decision. . . . An experience extending over more than seventy years has demonstrated that those who send in solutions of these problems understand neither their nature nor their difficulties, that none of the methods employed by them could ever lead to solutions of these problems, even were such solutions attainable. This long experience has convinced the Academy of the little value that would accrue to science, were the examination of these pretended solutions to be continued."

"There are still other considerations that have determined this decision. A popular rumour has it that the Government has promised considerable rewards to one who would first solve the problem of squaring the circle. . . . On the strength of this rumour, a multitude of people, much greater than is commonly believed, have given up useful work to devote their time to this problem which often they do not understand, and for which none of them possess the requisite preparation. Nothing could, therefore, serve better to discourage these people than this declaration of the Academy. Some of these individuals, being unfortunate enough to believe that they have been successful, have refused to listen to the criticism of geometers, often because they could not understand it, and have finished by accusing the examiners of envy and bad faith. . . ."

"The folly of the Circle-Squarers would result in no greater inconvenience than the loss of their own time at the expense of their families, were it not that such folly is, unfortunately, never confined to one subject, since the habit of fallacious thinking, even as that of correct reasoning, has a tendency to increase, as it has happened in more than one case. Moreover, to account for the singular fact that without studying the subject they have arrived at solutions which the most famous scholars have vainly sought—they persuade themselves that they are under the special protection of Providence, and from this there is but one step to the belief that any combination of ideas, however strange, that may occur to them are so many inspirations. Humane consideration therefore demanded that the Academy, persuaded of the uselessness of such examinations, should seek to offset by public announcement a popular opinion that has been detrimental to so many families. . . ."

"Such were the principal reasons that have determined the Academy's decision. The declaration that it will not engage in the future in this task is tantamount to a declaration that it regards as futile the work of those who engage in it. It has been often said that, while seeking chimerical solutions, one may discover a useful truth. Such opinions might have been valid in days when the methods for discovering truth were equally unknown in all fields of endeavour; today, when these methods are known, it is more than probable that the surest way to find truth is to seek it. . . ."

9

This long-forgotten document reads as though it had been written yesterday, and not 180 years ago. What effect did it have? Well, if the aim of the academicians was to spare the scientific societies the annoyance incident to the examination of these solutions, then they have been more than successful. Soon, other academies followed suit, until today it is impossible for a pseudomath to get a hearing before any reputable scientific organization. If, however, the French Academy had hoped to free the world from the pseudomath, then it must be admitted that the document was a miserable failure. For, I dare say, there are more pseudomaths today than at any time in history; besides, their numbers increase by leaps and bounds from year to year, while the negative attitude of the scientific world, far from dampening their ardour, only makes them more militant.

All this in spite of the fact that in the course of the last century all the problems reviewed by Condorcet were brought to a successful conclusion. For the pseudomath, time has stood still. The solutions of these problems may appear to the mathematician ever so profound and far-reaching; to the pseudomath they are but mockeries, delusions and snares, to use an expression of that king circle-squarer, James Smith.

And, strange as it may seem, these sentiments are shared by the public at large. Indeed, the solutions which modern mathematics has offered to the *famous problems* are not solutions at all, as the term is usually understood. They do not culminate in a definite recipe prescribing certain traditional operations on certain traditional ingredients; they culminate in the declaration that such a recipe is unattainable. Moreover, the reasoning which leads to these negative conclusions involves consideration of algebra and analysis which appear to the layman as irrelevant and, therefore, wholly unconvincing. The pseudo-math brushes all such reasoning away with a contemptuous smile, branding it professional subterfuge which aims at covering the orthodox mathematician's incompetence behind a smoke screen of symbols and technicalities.

10

And so the merry-go-round spins on. Each year sees new solutions of the ancient problems which the benighted mathematician has long ago stricken off his list as solved. Our own century has been particularly prolific: dozens of solutions have been announced in our daily press. One of these received extraordinary publicity. It concerned the trisection problem and was the discovery of a president of an American Catholic college. Substantially, the reverend father's solution consisted in trebling an angle, and then exclaiming: "Behold the whole, and then behold the part!" Judging from the numerous inquiries I have received concerning it, the pater's fame must have travelled very far. He was, in fact, so encouraged by the reception accorded to his achievement that he decided to continue his researches, and subsequently enriched the world with a book in which he proved the Euclidean postulate of parallels and, simultaneously, annihilated the impious Einstein.

I shall conclude this chapter by recording three conversations which I had, all in connection with this ecclesiastic trisection. My interlocutors were all college graduates. The first, a successful engineer, after listening to my explanation with ill-concealed irritation, interrupted me with a sneer: "The dogmatism of you fellows makes me tired. It reminds me of those experts who only twenty-odd years ago maintained that flying was impossible. Granted that the priest's construction is wrong, as were the other solutions before him; what of it? To me, it only means that the problem is a challenge to human ingenuity. I am confident that some day solutions to these problems will be found, and, that when they are found, it will not be along the beaten paths which the professional mathematician is bound to follow."

The second, a literary man with philosophical aspirations, said: "I cannot agree with your conclusions. It seems to me that mathematicians lose sight of one incontrovertible truth, namely, that *if a problem can be formulated in certain terms, it can be solved in the same terms.* Now, you admit that all the problems which you have mentioned can be formulated in terms of straight lines and circles; by the same token, their solutions should require no other lines."

The third, a realtor, listened to my comments with complacent mistrust. By way of changing the topic, or perhaps with a more subtle intent, he remarked that the college which the reverend father was heading possessed a first-class football team.

Chapter Seven

THE INTERDICTION

Indeed, when in the course of a mathematical investigation we encounter a problem or conjecture a
theorem, our minds will not rest until the problem is
exhaustively solved and the theorem rigorously proved;
or else, until we have found the reasons which made
success impossible and, hence, failure unavoidable.
Thus, the proofs of the impossibility of certain solutions
plays a predominant role in modern mathematics;
the search for an answer to such questions has often led
to the discovery of newer and more fruitful fields of
endeavour.   DAVID HILBERT

I

One who contemplates the silhouetted skyline of a great city
is struck with the abundance of the straight and the round to
the practical exclusion of all other forms. In distant outline, the
city looms as a monotony of rectilinear segments, relieved by
an occasional arc of a circle.

This preponderance of the straight and the round is not
limited to the contours of the buildings where we dwell or
work; the intricate equipment designed to aid us in our
struggle for existence, the vehicles which transport us from
place to place, the roads we travel, the games we play, the very
shape of our rooms, and of the furniture, utensils and trinkets
which crowd them bespeak this predilection.

Even more amazing is the spectacle which awaits one behind
the walls of our mills and shops. Round and round and to and
fro whirl and swing the machines, lathes, drills, shapers,
presses, ceaselessly engaged in flattening, straightening and
turning the raw materials furnished by nature.

Indeed, to a thinking being from another planet, unaware

of our human purposes, the complex activity which we call civilization might appear as a concerted effort to force upon Nature, irregular in her deeds and unruly in her moods, the acceptance of these forms preferred by man.

2

Nor is this preference an outgrowth of modern life. The machine age has only accentuated what has for millennia been latent in the human spirit. It is detected in the crude patterns of the savage, in the figures drawn on the walls of prehistoric caves. The utensils of bygone ages spared by the ravages of time bear mute testimony to this predilection. It is as though man has ever striven toward these forms as ideals, and the extent to which he has put them to use may be taken as indices of his knowledge and skill at various stages of his progress.

Already in the naïve endeavours of the primitive mind just awakened to the consciousness of form, in these groping efforts of an untutored imagination, we find, in germ, the elements which were destined to become the foundation of a great science. As time went on, these preferred forms came to be viewed by man not merely as indispensable principles of design and construction but as basic elements for an accurate description of nature. To these elements he endeavoured to reduce the complex forms which he encountered in experience, and out of these endeavours grew a science which, armed and guided by number, eventually attained the highest levels of abstraction.

It would be fitting to call this body of knowledge *the science of form*, but, because of long historical association, it has been identified with one of its earliest applications, *geometry, the measurement of earth*. Under this modest name, and with such modest beginnings, it has gradually extended its influence over the physical sciences until today it bids fair to dominate any rational interpretation of nature.

Yet, throughout this long evolution and to this day, the science has, in one respect at least, preserved its original character: the *flat*, the *straight* and the *round*, in the new guises of *spaces*, their *geodesics* and their *curvatures*, are concepts as basic in this *cosmic geometry* as they were in the rudimentary stages of the science.

3

What has forced this choice upon man?

One turns his back on the skyline of the great city to view the peaceful landscape beyond, the winding rivers, the rolling hillsides, the patches of marshes and forests. One contemplates the surrounding flora and fauna; the oddly shaped roots and stems and leaves and blades; the limbs and wings and bodies of beast and fowl and fish and of all that creepeth upon the earth. No! It was not here that man has found models for the severe line or the smoothly rolling circle, these preferred elements of his manipulation and speculation.

Why then has this distinction fallen to the lot of these special forms, so rarely encountered in man's natural environment? What is the source of this predilection, so manifest in the things which he has built for sustenance, comfort or defence? Why have these forms been chosen by man as cornerstones of that grandiose scheme of his own making which he seeks to identify with the physical universe?

4

In Ancient Greece, where stood the cradle of science, the preference for the straight and the round took the form of an interdiction: the line and the circle alone could be used in geometric construction; all other devices, regardless of their effectiveness or scope, were condemned as *mechanical* and unworthy of the philosopher.

According to Plutarch, we owe this proscription to Plato: "Eudoxus and Archytas had recourse to mechanical arrangements, adopting to their purpose certain curved lines and sections. But Plato inveighed against them with great indignation and persistence, as destroyers and perverters of all that was good in geometry, which was thus lowered from the incorporeal and intellectual to things material, and employed besides much mean and vulgar labour. In this manner, mechanics was dissimulated and expelled from geometry, and, being for a long time looked down upon by philosophers, it became one of the arts of war."

Now, in appraising the historical value of these statements, it should be remembered that in the course of the five hundred years which separated Plutarch from Plato, the latter had become somewhat of a legendary figure whose authority was often invoked by contending philosophical schools in support of views he had never uttered during his lifetime. Thus, we find that other Greek historians were by no means so emphatic in attributing to Plato the authorship of the interdiction. Indeed, some go so far as to accuse the Athenian philosopher of having himself at one time indulged in these mechanical solutions so unbecoming to a geometer and gentleman.

5

Whoever might have been the author of this drastic decree, there is ample evidence that, unlike most prohibitions, this one was eminently successful. In fact, it is impossible to overestimate the influence which the interdiction exerted on the subsequent course of geometry, and, strange as it may seem, its effect on postclassical geometry was even greater than it had been during the Hellenic period. Indeed, while the proscription did succeed in drawing a very sharp demarcation between what we now designate as elementary geometry, where the line and the circle rule supreme, and the other branches of the science—a demarcation which remains nearly intact today—it did not prevent the Greek geometers from mastering the forbidden curves of which Plutarch spoke.

Thus, as I already pointed out in a previous chapter, the same Euclid, whose *Elements* served for two thousand years as a model for textbooks in elementary geometry, wrote a treatise on the *conic sections* which, unfortunately, did not come down to us. The great Apollonius of Perga turned the study of these sections into a discipline as rigorous and fertile as the Euclidean *Elements*. What is more, the Greek geometers were even familiar with higher curves; the curved lines of which Plutarch spoke are designated today as *cubics*, while the *quadratrix* of the Sophist Hippias is of a type called today *transcendental*.

6

During the many centuries of decay which succeeded the Greek period, the achievements just mentioned had been all but forgotten, and when, with the revival of learning, the study of mathematics was again taken up, the line of demaraction between elementary geometry and the other branches of the science became sharper than ever.

To this day we say that such and such a problem is susceptible of a "geometrical" solution, when all we mean is that the required construction can be executed by means of the two traditional instruments—the *straightedge* and the *compass*. Another construction which may be effectively executed by means of devices as simple as either the straightedge or the compass we brand as impossible, only because the traditional instruments do not suffice here.

This unhappy terminology contributes much to the confusion which the general public entertains in matters mathematical. The layman hears that certain problems bequeathed to us by antiquity are spoken of by mathematicians as *impossible*: he naturally concludes that these problems still remain *unsolved*. The fact that the last of these questions, the squaring of the circle, has been a closed issue for more than fifty years is rarely, if ever, conveyed to him. The door is thus left wide open for quacks to enter with their preposterous or fraudulent solutions of problems which demonstrably admit of no solution in the traditional sense of the word.

The mathematical curricula of our schools and colleges, far from tending to dispel this confusion, indirectly add to it. However defective may be our school curricula, geography is not being taught out of Ptolemy, nor physics out of Aristotle; yet, as far as geometry is concerned, we are still in the Scholastic era. The textbooks used in our schools are but pale replicas of Euclid's *Elements* compiled by schoolteachers, most of whom are wholly unaware of the gigantic strides which geometry has made in the last few hundred years. As a result, the average layman leaves school under the impression that all that can be done in geometry has already been done two thousand years ago, with the exception of a few problems, such as the trisection of the angle, which still await a solution; and that here, the experts have admittedly failed, the mantle of glory is to fall on the shoulders of some amateur unpolluted by the hackneyed habits of the professional mathematician.

7

It is a striking phenomenon, to say the least: here is a discipline which in modern times has so enormously increased its scope as to cause a veritable revolution in the scientific outlook on the universe, and yet, as far as its teaching is concerned, we might as well be in the days of ancient Alexandria. To say that the conservatism of our school authorities is responsible for this state of affairs is but to christen the difficulty. A conservatism so universal and so deep-seated as to withstand the onslaught of progress for so many centuries must have its roots in some inherent predilection of the human mind.

Thus arises the question: Is there any connection between this deep-seated conservatism which has limited the general instruction in geometry to the properties of the line and the circle, this ancient interdiction which has proscribed the use of all instruments and devices other than the straightedge and the compass, and this inherent preference of man for the straight and the round so manifest in his work and his thought?

8

At the risk of boring the more sophisticated reader by belabouring the obvious, I must insist that the difficulties to which the celebrated problems of construction lead, far from being inherent in the problems themselves, merely reflect the drastic character of the restrictions imposed on classical construction; that the terms *possible* and *impossible* possess no *absolute* significance; that it is essential, in formulating any individual problem, to stipulate the *equipment* by means of which the construction is to be executed; that with all restrictions removed, with any device susceptible of mathematical definition admitted into geometry on equal terms with the straightedge and compass, and with any locus accepted on par with the line and the circle regardless of the mechanical or graphical procedure used in generating it, the terms possible or impossible lose all meaning, and the field of *soluble* problems becomes coextensive with the field of *all* problems.

These statements are truisms, I admit. And yet, there are truisms which cannot be overemphasized or repeated too often. To this class belong those verities which stipulate the *relative* character of concepts. So intense, indeed, is man's craving for the *absolute* that his intuition is ever ready to accept arguments which his reason would unhesitatingly reject. The history of such concepts as the *relativity* of *space* and *time* furnishes eloquent evidence to this tendency of the human mind.

9

In the light of these general observations, we should first of all examine the *scopes* of the traditional instruments with the view of ascertaining the limitations which their exclusive use imposed on geometrical activity. And since the restriction originated in Greece, we should begin by consulting Greek sources. Strangely enough, we find that, despite the exclusive roles which the straightedge and the compass played in classical geometry, classical treatises rarely, if ever, mentioned these instruments by name. In Euclid's *Elements* the equipment was introduced in the guise of *postulates* or *common notions*. The use of the straightedge was sanctioned in statements that any *straight line* could be produced indefinitely, that through any two points a straight line could be drawn, and that two straight lines would merge throughout if two points on one coincided with two points on the other. The use of the compass was sanctioned in the statements that it was possible to draw a circle which had its centre in any point and which passed through any other point, and that only one such circle existed.

As opposed to this classical tendency to keep the instruments in the background, the modern approach to geometrical construction puts the equipment prominently to the fore. In fact, the whole question could be reduced to the classification of problems according to the equipment they require. We could begin by separating problems which are susceptible of straight-edge-compass solutions from those which involve more intricate apparatus. These "higher" problems could, in turn, be grouped according to the character of the instruments which their solutions demand. For example, while the general angle may be trisected by a *linkage*, no circle can be squared by such means; the latter problem may be solved, however, by means of a *rolling* mechanism, while certain other constructions necessitate the introduction of *sliding* devices. We would thus have *linkage problems*, *roller problems*, *slide problems* and many others, their variety limited only by human resourcefulness.

10

Now, any classification scheme, no matter how cleverly contrived, is but an empty formality unless it is supported by definite *criteria*, i.e., by a code of unequivocal rules which any competent person may use to ascertain whether or not a given object belongs to a given class. As applied to our own programme, this means that we should begin by seeking *criteria of constructibility by straightedge and compass*. It is here that we encounter our first difficulty.

There is nothing, indeed, in the formulation of a construction problem to indicate whether it can or cannot be solved by means of the traditional instruments. The use of ruler and compass enables one to *trisect* any rectilinear segment, but not the general circular arc; to *inscribe* into a circle a regular polygon of 3, 5 or 17 sides, but not one of 7, 9 or 11 sides; to *square* any parabolic arch, but not a circle. Such facts are not of the sort that may be deduced from the statement of a problem, nor from the casual inspection of a hypothetical figure; they require, as a rule, a more or less intricate and seemingly artificial *reformulation of the problem in terms of algebra*, and sometimes in terms of *analysis*.

Is this devious approach unavoidable? The history of the celebrated problems gives a pragmatic answer to this query. For, in spite of the valiant attempts of Greek geometers, the problems remained at a virtual standstill for nearly two thousand years and were not completely solved until algebra and analysis had sufficiently advanced to be enlisted as effective allies.

As we proceed with this survey, we shall encounter many problems which reveal the difficulties inherent in a strictly geometrical approach to construction, and, incidentally, the reasons why the geometers of antiquity failed to resolve these difficulties. These problems will bring out in sharper relief the intimate kinship between geometrical construction, on the one hand, and the classification of numbers according to their *character*, on the other. In the last analysis a geometrical instrument can be identified with a category of numbers; thus, *any restriction imposed on equipment is a restriction on number*.

PART II

AN ANTHOLOGY OF THE
GREEK BEQUEST

Chapter Eight

THE HYPOTENUSE THEOREM

The Elements: hardly another scientific work has so long maintained so eminent a place in its field. Indeed, even today every mathematician must in one way or another come to terms with Euclid.

FELIX KLEIN

I

No other proposition of geometry has exerted so much influence on so many branches of mathematics as has the simple quadratic formula known as the Pythagorean theorem. Indeed, much of the history of classical mathematics, and of modern mathematics, too, for that matter, could be written around that proposition.

To begin with, it is the point of departure of most *metric* relations in geometry, i.e., of those properties of configurations which are reducible to magnitude and measure. For such figures as are at all amenable to study by classical methods are either polygons or limits of polygons; and whether the method be *congruence*, *areal equivalence* or *similitude*, it rests, in the last analysis, on the possibility of resolving a figure into triangles.

Next, the Pythagorean equation being *non-linear*, its numerical applications lead to *irrational* numbers. In this way mathematics, almost from its inception, was confronted with the perplexing problem of incommensurable magnitudes, and this exerted a profound, even if perturbing, influence on the evolution of the number concept.

Again, to determine all integral solutions of the equation

$$x^2 + y^2 = R^2 \qquad . \qquad . \qquad . \qquad (8 \cdot 1)$$

was one of the earliest problems in that branch of mathematics which came to be known as *number theory*. With the revival of mathematics, it led to the more general problem of determining integral solutions of the equation

$$x^n + y^n = R^n \qquad . \qquad . \qquad . \qquad (8 \cdot 2)$$

for *any integral value* of the exponent n. The statement that no such *triples* exist for exponents greater than 2 is known as *Fermat's theorem*. It remains in the realm of conjecture to this day.

With the advent of analytic geometry, the metric aspect of the theorem was greatly enhanced. A direct application of the theorem leads to the *distance formula* by means of which the length of any segment can be calculated in terms of the coordinates of its *end points*. Eventually, the equation has come to be viewed as the analytical representative of the *circles* in the plane, and this, in turn, has led to the fertile idea of describing and classifying geometrical loci by means of algebraic equations. To the same order of ideas belongs the notion of *absolute value* of a complex magnitude which plays such an important role in the theory of functions.

The introduction of infinitesimal methods led to further extensions of the formula's scope. In the guise of a *differential* form, it became the measure of the *length of the arc* of a plane curve. The idea was eventually extended to space curves, then generalized to curved surfaces.

Last but not least was the influence of the Pythagorean theorem on the so-called *non-Euclidean* geometries. When the axioms of geometry began to be subjected to a critical analysis, it was soon realized that the Pythagorean relation between the sides of a right triangle was equivalent to the Euclidean *postulate of parallels*. Thus, if one was to reject this postulate but retain the other axioms, one would have to replace the Pythagorean relation by another form. These considerations had led Riemann to the epoch-making idea of defining *space structures* by means of quadratic forms, an idea which, when extended to *space-time* manifolds, became the foundation of the *mathematical theory of relativity*.

2

Let us examine the two proofs of the Pythagorean proposition which have been attributed to Euclid. I use the word attributed advisedly, because there are definite indications that the proof at the end of Book One of the *Elements* was first advanced by the brilliant geometer Eudoxus who antedates Euclid by a generation at least, while the *similitude proof* of Book Six bears the marks of the Founder, Thales.

The characteristic feature of the first proof is that it interprets the Pythagorean theorem not as a *metric* relation between the sides of a right triangle but as a property of the *squares* erected on these sides. This literal interpretation of the theorem restricts the proof to *areal equivalence*. Now, to prove that noncongruent polygons contain the same area requires, as a rule, intermediate steps and auxiliary lines, which complicate the argument and obscure the figure. This may explain why the proof of Book One has been a source of despair to so many beginners, and why even those who have grasped it can rarely throw off the feeling that the proof is artificial and unnecessarily intricate. Thus, the caustic German philosopher Schopenhauer dismissed the demonstration with the contemptuous remark that it was not an argument but a "mousetrap."

Many a textbook on geometry has been written in the twenty-two-hundred-odd years since Euclid's work appeared. Some are mere facsimiles, others but blind adaptations of the *Elements*. Still, there are quite a few among these that make some pretence to originality. But even the latter present the "mousetrap" as *the proof* of the Pythagorean theorem, while the elegant demonstration of Book Six is rarely, if ever, mentioned. And yet, not only is this alternate proof superbly simple, but, by identifying the Pythagorean relation with the *existence of similar figures*, it strikes at the very root of the question. Paraphrased in modern terms, this means that in a geometrical field where two figures cannot be similar without being congruent at the same time, the relation between the sides of a right triangle would not be of the Pythagorean form.

The similitude proof, Proposition 31 of Book Six of the *Elements*, derives from a property which is characteristic of right triangles. The principle is illustrated in Figure 11. The perpendicular dropped from the vertex C of the right angle onto the

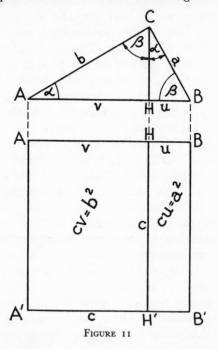

FIGURE 11

hypotenuse partitions ABC into the two right triangles AHC and BHC; either of these is *equiangular* with the original triangle and, therefore, *similar* to it. Hence the two proportions,

$$u : a = a : c, \text{ and } v : b = b : c.$$

From these we draw

$$a^2 = cu, \text{ and } b^2 = cv,$$

and, by addition,

$$a^2 + b^2 = c(u + v) = c^2.$$

Figure 11 gives an interpretation of these relations in terms of areas. The extended altitude of the triangle ABC partitions the square erected on the hypotenuse into the two rectangles (HA') and (HB'); in virtue of the preceding relations, the areas of these rectangles are a^2 and b^2, respectively. This, as we shall presently see, is the property which Euclid in his earlier proof sought to establish, but without the benefit of similar triangles.

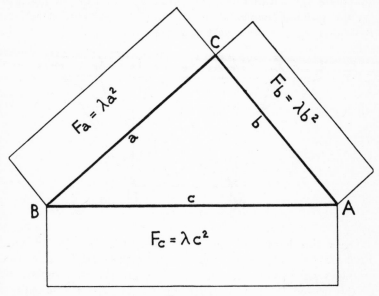

FIGURE 12

As a matter of record, to Euclid the proposition of Book Six was a generalization of the Pythagorean theorem rather than an alternate proof. Here is his wording: "In right-angled triangles, the rectilinear figure erected on the hypotenuse is equal to the similar and similarly described figures upon the sides containing the right angle." The drawing in the *Elements* shows three similar rectangles (Figure 12). However, the "described figures" could be equilateral triangles, or, for that matter, three semicircles.

4

The key to the *areal proof* of the Pythagorean theorem, Proposition 47 of Book One of the *Elements*, is a lemma which permits one to transform any given triangle into another equal to it in area but not necessarily congruent to it. The lemma is exhibited in Figure 13, where MN is a fixed segment, xx an indefinite line parallel to MN, and X any point on the line xx. As the point X moves along the line, the triangle MXN is deformed, but *its area remains unaltered*.

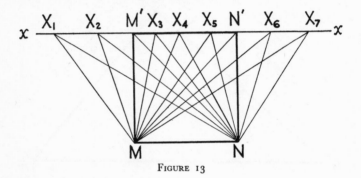

FIGURE 13

Once this lemma is borne in mind, the *stratagem* of the Euclidean proof becomes clear. The aim is to establish that the triangles HBQ and MBN in Figure 14 are *equiareal*. In virtue of the preceding lemma, HBQ can be replaced by the equivalent triangle CBQ, and MNB by the, equivalent triangle ANB. However, in the triangles CBQ and ANB we have:

$$AB = QB,\ CB = BN,\ \text{and angle } QBC = \text{angle } ABN;$$

thus CBQ and ANB are *congruent* and, therefore, *equiareal*. Passing from triangles to rectangles, one finds $BHKQ$ equal to $BCMN$, and, by analogous reasoning, $AHKP$ equal to $ACUUV$.

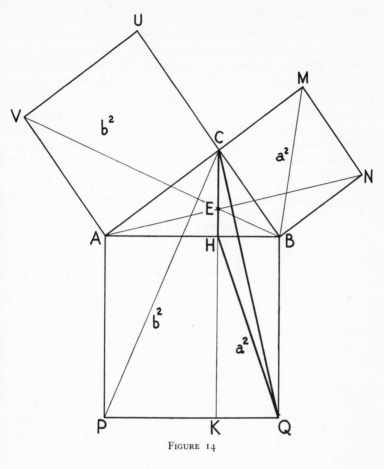

FIGURE 14

5

Why did Euclid place the intricate areal proof in the foreground, relegating the simple similitude proof to the very end of his study on similar figures? The answer is that the author of the *Elements*, with his customary thoroughness, would not deal with relations which depended on the *principle of similitude* until he had made an exhaustive study of *ratios* and *proportions*. Book Five of the *Elements* is just such a study.

One who reads the *Elements* today is amazed at the pains-taking care and tedious detail with which Euclid treats certain notions, notions which modern curricula dismiss with a few casual remarks. Particularly perplexing is the bewildering variety of special cases handled, cases which we would regard as but trivial variations of a general rule. One explanation of this apparent verbosity is to be found in the rudimentary state of Greek algebra. In the absence of an adequate symbolism, Greek mathematicians resorted to verbal procedures; these were eventually codified into a glossary of terms and rules most of which strikes us today as utterly superfluous and hence unintelligible.

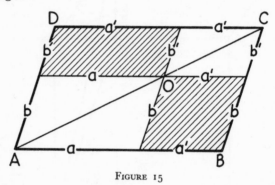

FIGURE 15

A case in point is the *theory of proportions* which constituted a very important part of the *rhetorical algebra* used by Greek geometers to express *metric relations*. It is here that the discrepancy between classical and modern exposition appears most striking. To illustrate, consider the proportion, $a : b = a' : b'$, and its "counterpart," the equality, $ab' = a'b$. Observe the facility with which we pass from one of these expressions to the other, then reflect that what we view today as a trivial manipulation of algebra was to the Greeks a basic theorem of geometry.

The theorem assigns to any pair of *similar rectangles* another pair of rectangles, *equal in area*. Associated with this proposition is a configuration which is shown in Figure 15. Let O be any point inside the parallelogram *ABCD*: the lines through O drawn parallel to the sides of the parallelogram partition the latter into four equiangular parallelograms (OA), (OB), (OC) and (OD) which I shall call *cells* for short. The theorem in question is this: *If the cells* (OA) *and* (OC) *are similar, then the cells* (OB) *and* (OD) *are equiareal, and conversely.* The similarity condition is fulfilled if, and only if, the point O lies on one or the other of the diagonals of *ABCD*. One thus arrives at the geometrical counterpart of the relation:

$$a : b = a' : b' \text{ entails } ab' = a'b,$$

and conversely.

6

It would be a mistake, however, to ascribe Euclid's meticulous handling of proportions solely to the low state of Greek algebra. The truth is that the Greeks were reluctant to identify ratios with numbers, the compelling cause of this hesitancy being the existence of *incommensurable magnitudes*.

How could one define the ratio of a circumference of a circle to its diameter, or the ratio of the diagonal of a square to its side, for that matter, without resorting to *infinite processes* and their limits, with all the qualms that such notions are heir to? Euclid was a Platonist, and the echoes of the controversy engendered by the Zenonian paradoxes had not yet subsided in his time. And lest we be tempted to treat this caution with too much levity, let us recall the travails of the modern *theory of irrationals*, the critical studies of Weierstrass, Cantor, Dedekind and Poincaré, the *antinomies* and the bitter controversies which are still fresh in the memories of the older mathematicians of our generation.

7

Figure 16 is a schematic drawing of what may be called an "articulated" ruler. The longest link *AB* is 5 units long; the shorter links measure 3 and 4 units, respectively. If the outer links be revolved about the pivots *B* and *C* until their end

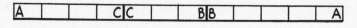

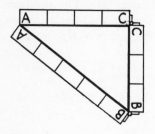

FIGURE 16

points meet in A, the resulting triangle ABC would have a right angle at C, in virtue of the identity,

$$3^2 + 4^2 = 5^2.$$

This method of constructing right angles antedates Pythagoras by thousands of years. It was used by ancient Egyptian surveyors in *orientation* problems; by the Chinese as a *levelling* device in masonry work; in other Oriental lands as sort of *carpenter square*. There is ample evidence that the ancients were aware of the existence of other *rational triangles*, such as are given by the triples (5, 12; 13) and (7, 24; 25), and it was, undoubtedly, the search of these triples that had led the early Greek mathematicians to the Pythagorean theorem.

The latter was a triumphant confirmation of the Pythagorean number philosophy. However, the triumph was short-lived, for, the very generality of the proposition revealed the existence of *irrational magnitudes*. One effect of this perturbing discovery was a revised outlook on matters of geometry. To the early Pythagoreans *every triangle was a rational triangle*, because they held that *all things measurable were commensurate*. This last dictum seemed to them as incontrovertible as any axiom, and when they proclaimed that *number ruled the universe*, they meant by number *integer*, since the very conception that magnitudes might exist which were not directly amenable to integers was alien to their outlook as well as to their experience.

8

Some modern interpreters of mathematical thought have been inclined to dismiss such ideas as naïve notions of a bygone age. And yet in the eyes of the individual who uses mathematical tools in his daily work—and his name today is legion—but to whom mathematics is but a means to an end and never an end in itself, these notions are neither obsolete nor naïve. For, such numbers as are of practical significance to him result either from *counting* or from *measuring* and are, therefore, either *integers* or *rational fractions*. To be sure, he may have learned to use with comparative facility symbols and terms which allude to the existence of nonrational entities, but this phraseology is to him but a useful turn of speech. In the end the rational number emerges as the only magnitude that can be put to practical use.

Should this individual, piqued by the reproach that he was naïve, endeavour to penetrate behind the mysterious nomenclature, he would soon discover that the processes invoked to vindicate these nonrational beings are wholly unattainable and, therefore, to him gratuitous. And yet, should he persist in his attempt to interpret such an entity in his own rational terms, he would be sternly reminded that in matters irrational one may at times *evade* the *infinite* but never *avoid* it. For, inherent in the very nature of this imponderable magnitude is the property that no matter how close any given rational number may "resemble" it, other rational numbers exist which "resemble" it even closer.

This individual would feel far more at home among the Pythagoreans than among their rigorous successors. He would willingly embrace their credo that all things measurable are commensurate. Indeed, he would be at a loss to understand why a principle so beautiful in its simplicity has been so wantonly discarded. And, in the end, the mathematician would be forced to concede that the principle was abandoned not because it contradicted experience, but because it was found to be incompatible with the axioms of geometry.

9

Indeed, if the axioms of geometry are valid, then the *Pythagorean theorem holds* without exceptions. And if the theorem holds, then the square erected on the diagonal of a square of side 1 is equal to 2. If, on the other hand, the *Pythagorean dictum held*, then 2 would be the square of some rational number, and this contradicts the tenets of rational arithmetic. Why? Because these tenets imply, among other things, that *any fraction can be reduced to lowest terms;* that at least one of the terms of such a reduced fraction is *odd;* that the square of an odd integer is odd; and that the square of an even integer is divisible by 4. Suppose then that there existed two integers, x and R, such that $R^2/x^2 = 2$, i.e., that

$$R^2 = 2x^2.$$

It would follow that R was even, and, since the fraction is in its lowest terms, that x was odd. One would thus be led to the untenable conclusion that the left side of an equality was divisible by 4, while the right was not.

The preceding argument is a modernized version of Euclid's proof of the *irrational character of* $\sqrt{2}$. Its very simplicity hints that it was but an adaptation of an earlier proof, perhaps, of the very one that had so profoundly perturbed the Pythagoreans and eventually forced them to change their outlook on number and measure.

Obviously, the reasoning is not limited to the case of an isosceles right triangle. Consider any right triangle the sides of which are integers, say x and y, but such that $x^2 + y^2$ *is not a perfect square:* by an argument patterned on that of Euclid it can be readily proved that such a triangle is not rational. This clearly reveals the existence of an infinitude of *non-rational triangles*. What is more, the preponderant majority of construction problems of classical geometry depended on just such nonrational triangles: it is sufficient to mention the *golden section*, the *regular polygons* and *bisection of standard angles*.

As a matter of fact, the determination of rational triangles is not a problem of geometry, since geometrically there is no way of distinguishing a rational triangle from any other. Nor is it a problem which algebra could resolve, inasmuch as the laws of formal algebra are obeyed by irrational numbers as well as rational. In the last analysis the problem is a study in *integers*.

Chapter Nine

TRIPLES

We found a beautiful and most general proposition, namely, that every integer is either a square, or the sum of two, three or at most four squares. This theorem depends on some of the most recondite mysteries of numbers, and it is not possible to present its proof on the margin of this page.

FERMAT

I

This chapter will deal with integers, more particularly with positive integers, i.e., with the "natural" sequence, 1, 2, 3, 4, . . . , the starting point of all mathematics. The branch of mathematics dedicated to the study of integers has come to be known as *theory of numbers*. The origin of this rather unhappy terminology is obscure, but one thing is certain: the misnomer cannot be blamed on the Greeks.

Classical Greek had two distinct words for number: *arithmos* for integer, *logos* for general number, and although in lay literature the two terms were at times loosely used, the mathematical writers were fairly consistent in distinguishing between their meanings. Thus the theory of numbers was called *arithmetica*, while what we today call arithmetic was then *logistica*. This last word, which has survived as a military term, may be traced to the Greek *logisticos, calculator*, more particularly a calculator attached to an army, charged with the planning, figuring and procuring supplies and equipment.

The misnomer harks back to an age when number meant *positive integer*, and little else. We have travelled a long way since; the evolution of the number concept has become one of the most profound, fertile and far-reaching mathematical studies, and it would be fitting indeed to call this larger study *theory of numbers*. So it is rather regrettable that the title has been pre-empted by a study which deals with integers exclusively. It may be argued that once this glaring misnomer has been recognized for what it is, it could be readily corrected, but one who harbours such thoughts underestimates the power of tradition, even in matters mathematical.

It is true that any systematic study of the general number concept must take the integer for point of departure, and so it may seem that the theory of integers is a sort of introduction to the *science of number*, and that as such it deserves the name bestowed upon it. We find, however, on closer scrutiny, that the chief preoccupation of the theory of numbers, as it is cultivated today, is not with *integers at large* but with particular types of integers, studied either individually or in sets. So special, indeed, are some of the problems of the theory that the keenest tools of analysis are often not keen enough to pierce the difficulty, with the result that quite a few of these problems remain unsolved to this day.

The challenge of these problems spurred the efforts of the greatest mathematicians from Fermat to Hilbert. Special methods of utmost ingenuity have been devised by these masters, and these methods have, in turn, enriched other branches of mathematics. With all that, the theory of numbers remains a sort of *sui generis* of mathematics, the magnificent pinnacle of an edifice rather than an integrated part of its structure. Like virtue, number theory is its own reward. Indeed, it is altogether possible to carry on studies in practically any branch of modern mathematics without ever facing the necessity of using number-theoretical tools. In this our age of extreme specialization, most mathematicians may safely remain ignorant of number theory, and most of them do. Gauss proclaimed the theory *Regina Mathematica*, but to the modern mathematician the queen is largely a figurehead.

2

The so-called Pythagorean problem may be stated as follows: to determine all integer sets which satisfy the equation

$$x^2 + y^2 = R^2 \qquad . \qquad . \qquad . \qquad (9.1)$$

I call such sets *Pythagorean triples*, or triples for short. The terms *x* and *y* are the *sides* of the triple, *R* its *hypotenuse*. Any triangle the sides of which can be represented by integers will be called a *rational* triangle. This does not restrict the scope of the term "*rational*," for if a triangle can be represented by means of *rational numbers*, i.e., integers and fractions, then it can also, through a proper change of unit, be represented by integers alone.

The branch of number theory which deals with integral solutions of equations is called *Diophantine analysis*, named after the Alexandrian mathematician of the fourth century A.D. who, as far as we know, was the first to attack such problems in a systematic manner.

The *Diophantine equation* (9.1) is of a special type called *homogeneous*. The important feature of such equations is this: if $(x, y; R)$ is a set of values which satisfy a homogeneous equation, then the *proportional* set $(nx, ny; nR)$ is also a solution of the equation, whatever value be assigned to *n*. Because of the homogeneous character of the Pythagorean relation, we can classify triples into *primitive* and *imprimitive*. A triple is primitive if its terms are *relatively prime*, i.e., have no divisors in common. On the contrary, the terms of an imprimitive triple have some divisors in common. Examples of primitive triples are (3, 4; 5), (5, 12; 13), (8, 15; 17); examples of imprimitive: (9, 12; 15), (10, 24; 26), (80, 150; 170).

Associated with every primitive triple $(x, y; R)$ is an infinitude of imprimitive: $(2x, 2y; 2R)$, $(3x, 3y; 3R)$, $(4x, 4y; 4R)$, . . . $(nx, ny; nR)$, ... On the other hand, if $(x, y; R)$ is an imprimitive triple, it is always possible to determine a primitive triple the terms of which are *proportional* to *x*, *y* and *R;* and this by the simple expedient of dividing every term of the triple by its *greatest common divisor*. I shall call this operation *contraction*.

Thus, whether any given triple is primitive or imprimitive depends on the value of its *greatest common divisor*. The labour incident to calculating this divisor is greatly facilitated by the following theorem, which is a direct consequence of the homogeneous form of the Pythagorean relation: *any integer which divides two terms of a Pythagorean triple also divides the third term.*

This theorem has two practical corollaries: *first*, to determine the greatest common divisor of a triple it is sufficient to calculate the greatest common divisor of any two terms of the triple; and *second, if any two terms of a triple are relatively prime then the triple is primitive*. As an example, consider the set $(140, 171; 221)$. Is it a triple, and if so, is the triple primitive? The set is a triple, because:

$$221^2 - 171^2 = (221 + 171)(221 - 171)$$
$$= 392 \cdot 50 = 196 \cdot 100 = 140^2;$$

and the triple is primitive, because 140 and 171 are *coprime*. On the other hand, the set $(36, 105; 111)$ is not primitive; its greatest common divisor is 3, and the *contracted primitive triple* is $(12, 35; 37)$.

3

A comprehensive solution of the Pythagorean equation was reserved for modern times. Though there are many allusions to the question in Book Ten of Euclid's *Elements*, in the *Arithmetica* of Diophantus and in several other mathematical tracts of the classical period, no systematic approach to the problem was even attempted. One reason for this was already brought out: considerations of *rationality* played a rather minor role in classical geometry, and geometry was the paramount interest of Greek mathematicians.

This much can be affirmed with certainty. The Greeks were fully aware of the importance of the concept of *primitivity;* they knew that *one of the sides of a primitive triple was even, the other odd, and that the hypotenuse was always odd*; they knew how to generate certain types of triples in number indefinite, and concluded from this that *the aggregate of primitive triples was infinite*. I shall elaborate somewhat on their arguments and methods, in modernized version, of course.

Let us take up the question of *parity* first. The case of three odd terms is out, on the ground that *the sum of two odd integers is even;* while the case of more than one even term is eliminated on the grounds of primitivity. Thus, there is only one even term, and it remains to show that it is not the hypotenuse.

Assume the contrary, and set $x = 2u + 1$, $y = 2v + 1$, $R = 2w$. Substituting, we obtain

$$4(u^2 + v^2 + u + v) + 2 = 4w^2,$$

which is untenable, since the right member is divisible by 4, while the left member is not.

Now, it has been conjectured that the Pythagoreans knew that *any odd integer may serve as one side of a primitive triple*, and that they discovered this property while seeking to determine triples two terms of which were *consecutive integers*. It is a plausible conjecture, because the proof of the theorem is quite within the ken of the period. Let us assume that y and R are the consecutive terms, and set $y = 2p$, $R = 2p + 1$. Then, substituting and solving the Pythagorean equation for x, we obtain $x = \sqrt{4p + 1}$. Now, *any odd square is of the form* 4p + 1, and consequently we can choose for x any odd integer. As an example, let us set $x = 9$: then $x^2 = 81$, and consequently $p = 20$; thus, $y = 40$ and $R = 41$. Generally, by setting $x = 2s + 1$, we obtain the triple

$$x = 2s + 1, \; y = 2s(s + 1), \; R = 2s^2 + 2s + 1. \quad . \quad (9.2)$$

These triples are primitive for all values of the *parameter s*, since *two consecutive integers are always relatively prime*. By varying s from 1 to ∞, we obtain an *infinite aggregate* of distinct primitive triples.

The Platonists, on the other hand, were more concerned with generating triples two terms of which were *consecutive odd integers*. Proceeding as before, we set

$$x = 2p - 1, \; R = 2p + 1,$$

and derive $y = 2\sqrt{2p}$. It follows that $2p$ must be an even square. By putting $2p = 4s^2$, we obtain the triple:

$$x = 4s^2 - 1, \; y = 4s, \; R = 4s^2 + 1; \quad . \quad (9.3)$$

and the set is primitive for any value of the *parameter s*, because *two consecutive odd integers are always coprime*. Thus there is a triple associated with every term of the progression

$$4, 8, 12, 16, \ldots, 4s, \ldots.$$

4

Fibonacci sought to extend the preceding results by determining primitive triples, given the difference between the hypotenuse and the even side, and discovered that the problem had no solution unless the *stipulated difference was itself a perfect square*. This led him to the idea of representing Pythagorean triples by means of *two parameters*, an idea which was a turning point in the history of the problem.

The official name of this gifted Italian mathematician of the early thirteenth century (perhaps the only European of the Middle Ages worthy of the title) was Leonardo of Pisa. His father was a lowly shipping clerk nicknamed Bonaccio, which, in the idiom of the period, meant *simpleton*. Hence, Fibonacci, *son of a simpleton*. Nor was this the only compliment paid to Leonardo by his fellow citizens: he was also called Bigollone, i.e., *blockhead*. In proud defiance of these indignities, Leonardo adopted both nicknames as pen names. The title of the book in which the ideas just mentioned were first introduced may sound quite glamorous in Latin, but an unvarnished translation would read: *A Book on Quadratics, Written by Leonardo the Block-head, Son of the Simpleton of Pisa*.

Fibonacci was the first to combine Greek achievements in geometry and number theory with the algebra of the Arabs and the positional numeration of the Hindus. In fact, his earlier work, *Liber Abacus*, should be viewed as an attempt at vindicating the *principle of position*. The book extols the many advantages of the new method over the traditional Roman numeration which was still widely used at the time; this may account for the abundance of examples drawn from the flourishing commercial life of the period. He also wrote a book on geometry, and while he added little to the store bequeathed by the Greeks, he was a pioneer in the applications of algebra to problems of geometry.

But his best contributions belong to number theory. It was he who conceived the idea of generating arithmetical sequences by means of *algorithms*. He knew many of the identities which we associate today with the names of Vieta, Euler or Lagrange, and made skilful use of these. It is true that his reasoning was occasionally tinged with error; still his demonstrations were, on the whole, remarkably rigorous for his period.

5

Fibonacci's approach to the Pythagorean problem is substantially this: let y be the even side of a primitive triple of hypotenuse R; then *the integers, $R + y$ and $R - y$ are relatively prime*, for, if they had a common divisor, say D, then D would divide their sum and their difference, i.e., $2R$ and $2y$, and this is impossible, since R and y are assumed coprime, and $R + y$ and $R - y$ are odd.

We next invoke a lemma which, in spite of its utmost simplicity, plays a capital role in many number-theoretical arguments: let $A, B, C, \ldots$ be any number of positive integers *with no divisors in common*; if

$$ABC, \ldots = S^n, \qquad \qquad (9.4)$$

i.e., *if the product of these integers is a perfect nth power, then each of the factors is an nth power "in its own right,"* and we may infer that

$$A = a^n, \; B = b^n, \; C = c^n, \ldots \qquad (9.4')$$

where $a, b, c, \ldots$ are also *relatively prime integers*.

As applied to the Pythagorean equation, we have

$$(R + y)(R - y) = R^2 - y^2 = x^2,$$

and we conclude of the existence of two integers u and v such that

$$R + y = u^2, \; R - y = v^2. \qquad (9.5)$$

Expressed in terms of these integers, the sides of the triple are

$$x = uv, \; 2y = u^2 - v^2, \; 2R = u^2 + v^2. \qquad (9.6)$$

Since u and v are odd, $u + v$ and $u - v$ are even. This suggests the substitution $u + v = 2p$, $u - v = 2q$, which puts (9.6) in the more convenient form

$$x = p^2 - q^2, \; y = 2pq, \; R = p^2 + q^2. \qquad (9.7)$$

A "random" choice of the integers p and q would yield a Pythagorean triple, but the triple would not be primitive, unless the parameters p and q were *relatively prime and of opposite parity*. Indeed, if p and q had a common divisor, say D, then D would also divide x, y and R; and if p and q were both odd, then $p^2 - q^2$ and $p^2 + q^2$ would be even. Thus, a *necessary condition for the primitivity of the triple represented by equations* (9.7) *is that one of the parameters be odd, the other even, and that the parameters be relatively prime*. These conditions are also sufficient.

6

The real significance of the Fibonacci approach is that it reduces the Pythagorean problem to "two degrees of freedom," and does it in an "exhaustive" manner. By this I mean that *any primitive solution* of the equation

$$x^2 + y^2 = R^2$$

can be expressed in terms of two integers p and q, the latter being coprime and of opposite parity.

The relation

$$R = p^2 + q^2 \quad . \quad \quad . \quad \quad . \quad (9.8)$$

suggests a systematic method of generating Pythagorean triples, as shown in the table on the following page: any entry is *the sum of an even and an odd square* and is, therefore, the hypotenuse of some triple. The "blanks" result from adding squares which are not coprime, and, therefore, correspond to imprimitive solutions.

7

To what extent does the knowledge of one term of a primitive triple determine the remaining two? The fundamental formulae of the preceding section answer this question as follows:

First: *Any odd integer is a side of at least one primitive triple.* Indeed, any odd integer may be written in the form

$$x = a^\alpha \, b^\beta \, c^\gamma \, \ldots = A \cdot B \cdot C \, \ldots \quad (9.9)$$

Hypotenuses of Primitive Triples: $R = p^2 + q^2$

		Even Squares					
		4	16	36	64	100	144 ...
	1	5	17	37	65	101	145 ...
	9	13	25		73	109	...
	25	29	41	61	89		169 ...
Odd Squares	49	53	65	85	113	149	193 ...
	81	85	97		145	181	...
	121	125	137	157	185	221	265 ...
	.	.	.	.	.	.	.
	.	.	.	.	.	.	.
	.	.	.	.	.	.	.

where $A, B, C, \ldots$ are odd integers, relatively prime in pairs. There are, generally, several ways in which x may be resolved into a product of two relatively prime integers, say M and N. For each one of these combinations, we may set $p + q = M$ and $p - q = N$, and obtain a distinct triple. One particular representation is $x = x \cdot 1$ and this leads to the triples considered in Section 3, in which the even side and the hypotenuse are *consecutive integers*.

Second: *If* y *is an even integer, but not a multiple of* 4, *then no solution of the Pythagorean equation exists*; *on the other hand, any multiple of* 4 *is a side of at least two primitive triples*. Indeed, any multiple of 4 may be written in the form

$$y = 2^k A \cdot B \cdot C \ldots;$$

hence

$$pq = \tfrac{1}{2} y = 2^{k-1} A \cdot B \cdot C \ldots \qquad . \quad (9.10)$$

where $k \geqslant 2$, and $A, B, C, \ldots$ are odd and relatively prime in pairs. Proceeding as before, we find that there are, generally, a variety of ways to present $\tfrac{1}{2} y$ as the product of two coprime factors of which one is even and the other odd. Among these there is always the choice $p = \tfrac{1}{2} y$, $q = 1$, and this leads to the

Platonist type discussed in Section 3, in which two terms are consecutive odd numbers; but there is also the choice: $p = 2^{k-1}$, $q = A \cdot B \cdot C$, ...

Third: Under what conditions will a given integer R *be the hypotenuse of some primitive triple?* One may say that R must be the sum of two relatively prime squares of opposite parity, but that, in a sense, is just begging the question. How, indeed, is one to ascertain whether a given odd integer R is or is not representable as a sum of two squares, particularly if R is large?

8

A partial answer to this question was a theorem which Fermat stated without proof in a letter to Father Mersenne, dated 1640. The proof was given by Euler in 1754, and later simplified and extended by Lagrange, Legendre and Gauss. It eventually led to far-reaching investigations into the *arithmetic properties of quadratic forms*. These, however, do not concern us here, and so I shall confine myself to a statement of Fermat's theorem and to an outline of its immediate applications to the Pythagorean problem.

Let us observe, first of all, that any odd number is either of the *type* $4n + 1$ or of the *type* $4n + 3$, which is but another way of saying that if an odd number is divided by 4, the *remainder* is either 1 or 3. In the second place, an *odd square* is necessarily of the type $4n + 1$, because

$$(2p + 1)^2 = 4p(p + 1) + 1 = 4n + 1.$$

Next, let us agree to designate as 2-*square* any integer which can be represented as the *sum of two squares*: then an *odd* 2-*square is always of type* $4n + 1$, since its components, p^2 and q^2, are of opposite parity. It follows that any admissible hypotenuse of a primitive triple is of type $4n + 1$, i.e., a term of the arithmetic progression

$$\underline{5}, 9, \underline{13}, \underline{17}, 21, \underline{25}, \underline{29}, 33, \underline{37}, \underline{41}, 45, 49, 53, 57, \underline{61}, \underline{65}, \ldots$$

.   .   .   (9.11)

117

The underlined numbers are 2-squares: observe that these integers are either *prime*, such as 5, 13, 17, 29, . . . , or *products of prime 2-squares*, such as 65, 85, 117, . . . , or *powers of prime 2-squares*, such as 25, 125, 169, ... It must have been such an empirical study that had led Fermat to his discovery.

9

Fermat's 2-squares theorem may be stated as follows: *any prime number of type* 4n + 1 *can be partitioned into a sum of two squares, and the partition is unique.* Conversely, if the equation

$$x^2 + y^2 = R \qquad . \qquad . \qquad . \qquad (9.12)$$

has only one solution in x and y, then R is a prime. Furthermore, if the equation (9.12) has any solutions at all, then R is either a *prime 2-square* or a *product of prime 2-squares*. The bearing of these propositions on the Pythagorean problem is this: *a necessary condition for an odd integer* R *to be the hypotenuse of a primitive triple is that every one of the prime divisors of* R *be of type* 4n + 1. This condition is also sufficient.

Thus the hypotenuse of a primitive triple *is not divisible* by 3, 7, 11, 19, or by any prime of type $4n + 3$. This restriction does not apply to the sides, x and y, of the triple. Indeed, one or the other of the sides must be a multiple of 3. This is a direct consequence of equations (9.7), according to which:

$$xy = 2pq(p^2 - q^2). \qquad . \qquad . \qquad . \qquad (9.13)$$

For, if p is not a multiple of 3, then p^2 is of type $3n + 1$; if neither p nor q is a multiple of 3, then both p^2 and q^2 are of type $3n + 1$, and, consequently, their difference is divisible by 3. Thus xy is always divisible by 3, and, as a matter of fact, by 12.

On the other hand, the hypotenuse R *may be* divisible by 5; what is more, one of the three terms of a primitive triple *must be* divisible by 5. Here is a simple "digital" proof of this: the *fourth power* of any integer p ends in 0 or 5, if p is divisible by 5; and ends in 1 or 6, if p is not. It follows that if neither p nor q is a multiple of 5 then $p^4 - q^4$ is divisible by 5. Thus if

118

the even side y is not a multiple of 5, then the product Rx is divisible by 5. As a combination of these properties we infer that *the product of the three terms of a primitive triple is always divisible by* 60, a fact which was known to Fibonacci.

10

In its formal aspects, the Fermat theorem is but a paraphrase of an algebraic identity which, in "rhetorical" form, was already used by Fibonacci, namely:

$$(p^2 + q^2)(p'^2 + q'^2) = (pp' + qq')^2 + (pq' - p'q)^2$$
$$= (pp' - qq')^2 + (pq' + p'q)^2. \quad (9.14)$$

In the special case when $p' = p$ and $q' = q$, the second part reduces to

$$(p^2 + q^2)^2 = (p^2 - q^2)^2 + (2pq)^2.$$

The last was used by Fibonacci to establish the *compatibility* of Equations (9.7). Yet, for all their importance, these identities are purely *formal*, by which I mean that they apply not only to integers but to *any entities which obey the laws of formal algebra*.

These identities show that the product of any number of odd 2-square integers is itself a 2-square, and, therefore, of type $4n + 1$. On the other hand, not every integer of this type is a 2-square. The crux of the difficulty lies in the circumstance that the product of two integers of type $4n + 3$ is of type $4n + 1$. For an odd integer R to be the sum of two squares it *must be* of the form $4n + 1$; but this is *not sufficient*. However, it is sufficient in the case when R is a *prime* number, and this is Fermat's theorem.

11

Viewing the problem in retrospect, can one claim that after engaging the efforts of first-rate mathematicians for twenty-five hundred years the Pythagorean equation has finally been exhaustively solved? The answer will depend on what one is willing to accept as *solution*. An odd integer R of type $4n + 1$ being given, the problem is to ascertain whether a primitive triple of hypotenuse R exists, and if it does exist, to determine the sides of the triple. Fermat's theorems reduce the question to determining the prime divisors of R, and this may at first sound like a solution of the problem. Unfortunately, it is one of those cases which were so aptly described by Eratosthenes as "replacing one perplexity by another even more perplexing." Indeed, not only do we lack effective criteria for testing the *primality* of integers, but the available practical means are so limited as to render the task formidable beyond imagination, when the integer exceeds 1,000,000.

To illustrate this last point, let us consider the integer 1,000,009. In a paper published in the year 1774, Euler listed this integer as prime. In a subsequent paper Euler corrected his error and gave the prime divisors of the integer, adding that at one time he had been under the impression that the integer in question admitted of the *unique partition*

$$(a) \qquad 1,000,009 = 1,000^2 + 3^2$$

but that he had since discovered a *second partition*, namely,

$$(b) \qquad 1,000,009 = 235^2 + 972^2,$$

which revealed the composite character of the number.

Euler then proceeded to calculate the divisors of 1,000,009 by a method patterned along the proof of a Fermat theorem which he gave in an earlier paper, and which stated that *if an odd integer R is susceptible of more than one partition into two squares, then R is composite.* The interesting thing about this method is that it not only proves the *existence* of the divisors but permits one to calculate them in terms of the elements of the given partitions. Thus in the case under consideration, Euler found

$$(c) \qquad 1,000,009 = 293 \times 3,413.$$

Since both divisors are prime numbers, no third partition exists.

Chapter Ten

THE CRESCENTS OF HIPPOCRATES

Geometry may at times appear to take the lead over analysis, but in fact precedes it only as a servant who goes before his master to clear the path and light him on the way.

JAMES SYLVESTER

I

He flourished in the middle of the fifth century B.C. as did that other Hippocrates, whose pledge healers honour, even in the breach. I doubt that the two had ever met or even heard of one another. Indeed, the name was common among ancient Greeks who, seemingly, held horse and horseman in much esteem; hence, "hippo" in prefix, as in Hippocrates, Hippias, Hipparchos; or in suffix, as in Philippos, Speusippos, Xanthippe.

Hippocrates, the geometer, haled from Chios, an island which lies a hundred-odd miles from Miletus, the birthplace of Thales. Indeed, the legend of his life resembles that of the Founder in more than one way. He, too, began as a merchant and ended up as a teacher; he, too, was initiated into the mysteries of number and extension after reaching maturity. However, his mentors were not priests but zealous followers of the Pythagorean doctrine which by that time had grown into a veritable cult. For, we are told that while on a visit to Athens he came in contact with a group of Pythagoreans who taught him what they knew of geometry and arithmetic; that having subsequently lost his fortune, he was reduced to selling these mathematical secrets to anyone who could and would pay the price, thus betraying his mentors' trust; that this sordid traffic had roused the righteous wrath of his erstwhile teachers who henceforth countered his achievements with contemptuous silence.

And how did he lose his fortune? Well, one version was that his ships had been plundered by pirates on the high seas; but Aristotle, who never missed a chance to vent his spleen against mathematicians, gave a less glamorous account of the event. "It is well known," he wrote, "that persons brilliant in one particular field may be quite stupid in most other respects. Thus Hippocrates, though skilled in geometry, was so supine and stupid that he let a customs collector of Byzantium swindle him out of a fortune."

The scope of his contributions is a moot question, for, while the Pythagoreans ignored his work, their opponents swung to the other extreme. He, allegedly, wrote a treatise on geometry, the first of its kind, where among many other innovations he introduced the use of capital letters to designate points on a figure. No trace of the textbook remains, but the technique of describing a figure by means of letters placed at salient points has since become universal.

He is credited by Eratosthenes with reducing the Delian riddle to the *insertion of two mean proportionals between a segment and its double*, thus paving the way to all subsequent solutions of the problem. Some assert that he was the first to prove that the area of a circle was equal to that of a triangle erected on the semicircumference as base and radius as altitude, thus reducing the problem of *squaring* a circle to the *rectification* of its boundary. Others go so far as to claim that he was the first to advance the epoch-making idea of viewing the area within a closed curve as the limit of a variable polygon inscribed in the boundary.

How much of this is fact and how much fancy we shall probably never know. So let us pass to the one achievement which both friend and foe associate with the name of the man: the *Hippocratean crescents*.

2

Broadly speaking, a *crescent* or *lune* is a portion of the plane bounded by two circular arcs. However, in what follows we shall be concerned only with the case when both arcs lie on one side of their common chord, *CD* in Figure 17. The axis of *symmetry* of the crescent, or *meniscos*, as the Greeks called it, contains the centres *A* and *B* of the circles, as well as the midpoints *E* and *F* of the arcs. In fact, the crescent is completely determined by the triangle *ABC;* and so the first step in *squaring the crescent* should be to express the area in terms of the elements of that triangle. Yet, Hippocrates did nothing of the sort; for that matter, he couldn't if he would, and wouldn't if he could.

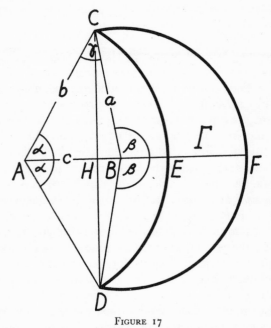

FIGURE 17

In the first place, the connection between the area of the crescent and the elements of the triangle involved concepts which lay beyond the scope of classical geometry. Indeed, denote by Γ the area of the crescent, by Δ the area of the quadrilateral *ACBD*, by a and b the radii of the circles, and by 2α and 2β the central angles subtended by the two arcs; then, a direct examination of the figure leads to the relation:

$$\Gamma + \text{Sector } CADEC = \Delta + \text{Sector } CBDFC.$$

From this we draw the formula

$$\Gamma = \Delta + (a^2\beta - b^2\alpha) = ab \sin (\beta - \alpha) + (a^2\beta - b^2\alpha),$$

.   .   .   (10.1)

a formula which involves the angles α and β not only through their trigonometric functions but *explicitly*. Such *goniometric* considerations, however, were beyond the ken of the Hippocratean period.

3

In the second place, Hippocrates was not concerned with the general crescent but with a very special kind, known as *quadrable*. Strictly speaking, a bounded region of the plane is *quadrable* if *a square of equal area can be constructed by straightedge and compass*. Any parallelogram is quadrable, because it can be converted into a rectangle of equal area, which, in turn, can be converted into a square, the side of the latter being the *mean proportional* between the sides of the rectangle. The same holds for any triangle, from which we conclude that *the area bounded by a general polygon is quadrable, provided that the polygon itself can be generated by straightedge-compass operations.* Another example of a quadrable area is the general *parabolic segment*, i.e., the region bounded by an arc of a parabola and the line which joins its end points, for, according to a celebrated theorem of Archimedes, *the area of a parabolic segment is equal to two thirds of the area of the triangle bounded by the chord and the tangents.* Examples of *nonquadrable areas* are the circle itself, or any sector or segment thereof constructible by straightedge and compass.

Thus, the existence of quadrable crescents is anything but evident. However, one such crescent is shown in Figure 18, and its utmost simplicity suggests that it was known before Hippocrates; for all we know, this crescent might have served as the point of departure of his investigation. Here the outer arc is a semicircumference, the inner a quadrant. A direct inspection of the figure shows that the area of the crescent is $\Gamma = a^2$, where a denotes the radius of the outer arc.

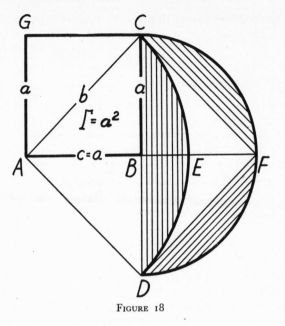

FIGURE 18

4

Some historians maintain that Hippocrates believed that the number of quadrable crescents was *infinite*. I find little evidence to support this contention, and even less to justify the sarcastic allegation of Aristotle that Hippocrates had invented his crescents for the express purpose of *squaring the circle*. On the other hand, it is quite possible that Hippocrates did not rule out the feasibility of squaring the circle, and that he used the crescents to demonstrate that circular and rectilinear figures may possess the same area. This would explain why he limited his study to a special variety of crescents which I shall call in what follows *Hippocratean*.

These special crescents satisfy the following conditions: *First, the sectors* which rest on the two arcs of the crescent, *ACED* and *BCFD* in Figure 17, are *equal in area*; and *second, the central angles* of these sectors are *commensurable*.

125

The first of these conditions, with the notations of formula (10.1), leads to

$$a^2\beta = b^2\alpha, \qquad . \qquad . \qquad . \qquad (10.2)$$

from which we conclude that

$$\Gamma = \Delta, \qquad . \qquad . \qquad . \qquad (10.3)$$

i.e., that *the area of a Hippocratean crescent is equal to the area of the quadrilateral bounded by the four radii which pass through its "horn-points."* Thus, such a *crescent is quadrable* if, and only if, the triangle *ABC* is *constructible by straightedge and compass.*

Applying the law of sines to the triangle *ABC*, we are led to the equation

$$\frac{\sin \alpha}{\sin \beta} = \sqrt{\frac{\alpha}{\beta}} \qquad . \qquad . \qquad . \qquad (10.4)$$

However, this interpretation does not solve the problem of quadrability: on the contrary, it merely accentuates the difficulty. The issue is this: *is it possible to express sin α and sin β in terms of rational numbers and quadratic surds?* This is not a question of geometry or algebra, or even analysis; it is a problem of *transcendental arithmetic*, a field of mathematics replete with questions that have challenged the keenest minds these last two centuries. Some few of these, such as the transcendental character of the numbers *e* and π, have been brought to a successful conclusion. However, the solutions were not of a type to suggest general methods for attacking kindred problems. Indeed, it may be stated without peradventure that transcendental arithmetic has more unsolved problems and unproved conjectures than any other branch of mathematics.

5

Assume next that the angles α and β are *commensurable*. This means that integers *p* and *q* exist such that

$$\alpha/p = \beta/q \text{ or } \alpha = p\omega, \ \beta = q\omega. \qquad . \qquad (10.5)$$

By substituting these values in (10.4) we put the latter in the form

$$q \sin^2 p\omega = p \sin^2 q\omega. \qquad . \qquad . \qquad (10.6)$$

This last relation may be viewed as the defining equation of all *Hippocratean crescents*, whether quadrable or nonquadrable. The integers p and q may, without loss of generality, be assumed relatively prime; i.e., angle ω may be viewed as the *greatest common measure* of α and β. The form of a Hippocratean crescent depends only on p and q; accordingly, I shall denote the crescent by the symbol (q, p), where q is the greater of the two numbers.

Equation (10.6) is transcendental in appearance only. We shall see, indeed, that it may be transformed by rather simple manipulations into an ordinary equation of degree $q - 1$. If this latter admits of a *rational root*, or of a root which may be expressed in terms of *quadratic surds* bearing on rational numbers, then the crescent is *quadrable*. If no such "admissible" root exists, then the crescent is *nonquadrable*.

6

How did Hippocrates cope with these difficulties? How did he stumble on the problem in the first place? What prompted him to pursue the quest? Was he aware that quadrable crescents existed for $q = 5$ but none for $q = 4$? Did he believe, as some commentators insist, in the existence of an infinite number of quadrable crescents? Did he restrict the problem to what we may call "algebraic" crescents, because he sensed that any other crescent is nonquadrable, or was he motivated by mere expediency?

On some of these points we have no knowledge whatsoever; on others the information is most sketchy and often conflicting, which is not surprising, since even the earliest commentaries on Hippocrates were written many centuries after his death. Now, an honest restoration of any work must cling tenaciously to the ken and spirit of the period which has given rise to the work. In the case of Hippocrates, however, we know very little of the ken of the period, and what little we do know is largely derived from speculations on his achievements. It is a vicious circle, indeed! And yet, so important are the Hippocratean methods to the understanding of Greek mathematics that I have resolved to risk here a partial restoration of his contributions to the problem.

7

Hippocrates based his arguments and constructions on certain theorems pertaining to *similar segments*. The term is rarely used today, but it played quite an important role in Greek speculations on squaring the circle. A *circular segment* is completely determined by the *radius* of the circle and the *angle* at which the chord is viewed from the centre of the circle. If two circular segments have equal radii and equal central angles, they are said to be *congruent*. If, on the other hand, they have equal central angles but unequal radii, they are said to be *similar*.

These statements sound like mere definitions, and yet they are more than that. Indeed, the extension of congruence and similitude from rectilinear to curvilinear figures—which, incidentally, has been attributed to Hippocrates himself—is accomplished through an *infinite process*, the arc of the curve being viewed as the *limit* of a variable polygonal contour. By the same token, the *metrical aspects of similarity*, which grew out of the theory of similar triangles and were eventually extended to similar polygons, are assumed to retain their validity for curvilinear configurations. The circular segment is a case in point: the arcs of two similar segments are proportional to their chords, while the *areas of similar segments vary as the squares erected on the chords*.

Consider now a crescent of the *commensurable* type. Denote, as before, by 2α and 2β the central angles, by 2ω the common measure of these angles, and set, as before, $\alpha = p\omega$, $\beta = q\omega$. Hippocrates begins by dividing the inner arc into p equal parts and joining the points of division by chords; in this manner he forms a system of congruent segments, each of radius a and central angle 2ω (Figure 19). He proceeds in the same manner with the outer arc, generating a system of q congruent segments each of radius b and central angle 2ω. It is obvious that the first system of segments lies *outside* the crescent, and it is not difficult to prove that the second system lies *entirely within* the crescent. Furthermore, any segment of

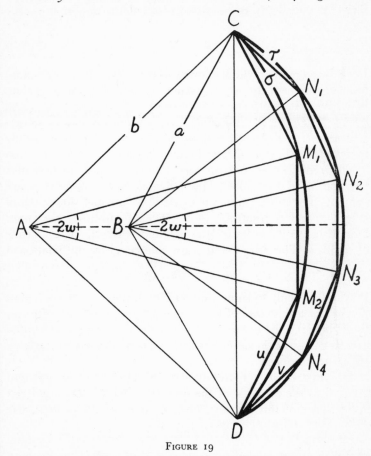

FIGURE 19

the first system is *similar* to any segment of the second, so that if we denote by u and v the respective chords of the two systems, and by σ and τ the areas of the respective segments, then, by the lemma mentioned above,

$$\sigma : \tau = u^2 : v^2. \qquad \qquad (10.7)$$

8

The next step in the Hippocratean reasoning is this: there exist, among the infinite variety of commensurable crescents, some for which the two systems of segments possess the same area, i.e.,

$$p\sigma = q\tau \qquad . \qquad . \qquad . \qquad (10.8)$$

Let Γ be a crescent which enjoys this property; then by deleting from the crescent the second system of segments, and adjoining to it the first, we form a *closed polygon of the same area as the crescent* Γ. *The crescent is quadrable, if the polygon is, and the polygon is quadrable, if its construction can be accomplished by means of the straightedge and compass.* (See Figure 19.)

This reduces the construction of crescent (q, p) to that of a polygon of $p + q$ sides. The polygon has a rather special contour. The outer branch is made up of q equal sides each of length u and is inscribed in a circle of radius a; the inner branch has equal sides of length u and is inscribed in a circle of radius b. The sides u and v are connected by the relation

$$u : v = \sqrt{q} : \sqrt{p} \qquad . \qquad . \qquad . \qquad (10.9)$$

It is not difficult to show that such "Hippocratean" polygons "exist" for any values of the integers p and q. But to state this is just begging the question. The issue is: *is the polygon associated with the crescent (q, p) quadrable?* i.e., can it be erected by straightedge and compass?

As a matter of fact, the area of the Hippocratean polygon is equal to the area, Δ, of the quadrilateral $ACBD$ considered in Section 4 of this chapter. For, in virtue of the proportions,

$$\alpha : \beta = p : q \text{ and } u : v = a : b$$

condition (10.9) is equivalent to $b^2\alpha = a^2\beta$, which, as we saw, entails $\Gamma = \Delta$. Thus *the Hippocratean polygon is constructible by straightedge and compass, if the quadrilateral is, and vice versa.*

On the other hand, while the two criteria of quadrability are theoretically equivalent, the construction techniques to which they lead are far from identical. This may appear as of little consequence to one who has all the devices of formal algebra at his fingertips and, hence, can pass from one approach to the other by a twist of the wrist, as it were. But to the classical geometer who had no other way of expressing *metric relations* than in the cumbersome language of a *graphical algebra*, the choice of method was not a mere matter of mathematical elegance.

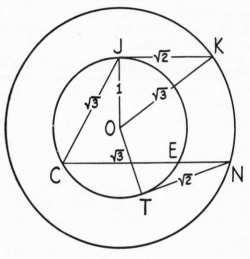

FIGURE 20

A case in point was the *quadratic equation*, or rather the classical equivalent thereof: a system of simultaneous equations, the prevailing types being

$$x + y = a, \ xy = c^2; \text{ and } x - y = b, \ xy = c^2 \quad . \quad (10.10)$$

where, of course, *a*, *b* and *c* were viewed as given rectilinear segments. The graphical solutions of these two basic problems is shown in Figure 20. The *mean proportional between two segments* is the key to both constructions. To us today this means a simple arithmetic operation, but Greek mathematicians regarded it as an important geometrical problem, and devised a variety of procedures to cope with it.

One such device, based on a theorem to which Greek

geometers attached considerable importance, is used in Figure 20 for the *graphical solution* of the *simultaneous equations*

$$x - y = \sqrt{3}, \ xy = 2, \qquad . \qquad . \qquad (10.11)$$

which, as we shall presently see, enter in the construction of crescents of type (3.2). The theorem in question may be stated as follows: *the tangent drawn from a point to a circle is the mean proportional between any transversal which passes through the point and its external part.* Thus in Figure 20: $NT^2 = NC.NE$.

In the figure, CE is the side of an equilateral triangle inscribed in a circle of radius 1, i.e., $CE = \sqrt{3}$. The larger concentric circle is of radius $\sqrt{3}$, and the tangent to the smaller circle issued from any point, K, on the larger circle is of length $\sqrt{2}$. It follows that the segments NC and NE give the graphical solution to (10.11).

10

For crescent of type (3.1), the Hippocratean polygon is a *trapezoid* with three sides of equal length. Denoting the latter by u, and setting $u = 1$, we find that the fourth side is $v = \sqrt{3}$. Or, as Hippocrates would have stated this: *the greater side of the trapezoid is to the lesser side as the side of an equilateral triangle is to the radius of the circle into which it is inscribed.*

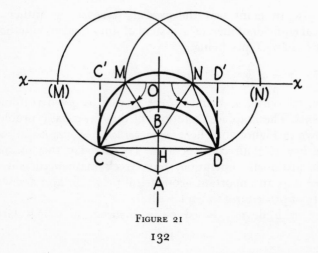

FIGURE 21

The construction of (3.1) is, therefore, direct and simple. (Figure 21.) On the carrier xx erect $MN = 1$ and $C'D' = \sqrt{3}$; with M and N as centres, draw the *unit circles* (M) and (N). The perpendiculars to xx erected at C' and D' meet these circles in the vertices C and D of the trapezoid sought. To determine the centre B of the crescent, draw the bisector of the angle at M; to locate the centre A, draw the perpendicular CA to CM.

For crescent of type (3.2), the *associated pentagon* is a sort of *truncated trapezoid: CEDNMC* in Figure 22. Indeed, by analysing the angles of the configuration, we find that the sides of the inner branch, CE and DE continued, pass through the vertices N and M of the outer branch. The same analysis shows that the sides CM and DN of the outer branch are tangent to the inner arc of the crescent. On the other hand, we have in virtue of (10.9), $u : v = \sqrt{2} : \sqrt{3}$. If then we set $u = \sqrt{2}$, $v = \sqrt{3}$, we find

$$\overline{CN} - \overline{EN} = \overline{CE} = \sqrt{3}, \ \overline{CN} \cdot \overline{EN} = \overline{ND^2} = 2 \ . \quad (10.11)$$

We are thus led to the simultaneous equations discussed in the preceding section and the graphical solution given in Figure 20.

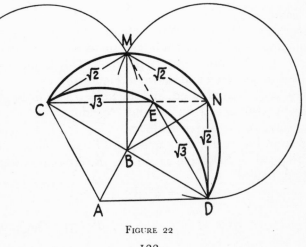

FIGURE 22

In Figure 22, the order of procedure is: (1) locate the points C, E and $\mathcal{N}$; (2) determine the remaining vertices, M and D; (3) the centre, B, of the outer arc is the intersection of the perpendicular bisectors to the diagonals $C\mathcal{N}$ and DM of the trapezoid; (4) the centre, A, of the inner arc of the crescent is obtained by erecting perpendiculars to CM and $D\mathcal{N}$.

The restorations exhibited in Figures 20, 21 and 22 are offered here for what they are worth. They are not based on any authentic information as to the actual methods used by Hippocrates, any more than are the sundry other restorations which have been proposed during the twenty-two centuries which separate the two periods. All I claim for my own con-jectures is that they do not transcend the ken of the period during which the problems were solved, as I envisage that ken.

II

Returning to the algebraic analysis of the Hippocratean problem, I take as defining equation the relation (10.4)

$$\frac{\sin \alpha}{\sin \beta} = \sqrt{\frac{\alpha}{\beta}}$$

established in Section 4.

Type (2.1): Here $\beta = 2\alpha$. Hence $\sin 2\alpha = \sqrt{2} \sin \alpha$. Eliminating the "trivial" solution $\sin \alpha = 0$, we arrive at $\cos \alpha = 1/\sqrt{2}$. Thus $\alpha = 45°$, $\beta = 90°$. This is the crescent discussed in Section 3 and shown in Figure 18.

Type (3.1): Here $\beta = 3\alpha$, and $\sin 3\alpha = \sqrt{3} \sin \alpha$. Replacing $\sin 3\alpha$ by $3 \sin \alpha - 4 \sin^3 \alpha$, and "shedding," as before, the trivial solution, we arrive at $\sin \alpha = \frac{1}{2}\sqrt{3 - \sqrt{3}}$. The crescent is shown in Figure 21: the angle γ at C is 2α. The area of the quadrilateral $ACBD$ being $ab \sin 2\alpha$, the crescent is *quadrable*. We find, indeed:

$$\Gamma = a^2 \, 3^{\frac{3}{4}} \, 2^{-\frac{1}{4}}.$$

Type (3.2): Here $\omega = \gamma$, $\alpha = 2\gamma$, $\beta = 3\gamma$. The equation,

$\sqrt{2}$ sin $3\gamma = \sqrt{3}$ sin 2γ, leads to a *quadratic* in cos $\gamma = x$, namely, $4x^2 - x\sqrt{6} - 1 = 0$. The result is

$$\cos \gamma = (\sqrt{22} + \sqrt{6})/8.$$

(see Figure 22)

The crescent is *quadrable* with

$$\Gamma = \tfrac{1}{8}\sqrt{18\sqrt{3} - 6\sqrt{11}}.$$

Type (4.1): Here $\beta = 4\alpha$, and sin $4\alpha = 2$ sin α. This leads to $4 \cos^3 \alpha - 2 \cos \alpha - 1 = 0$. If we set sec $\alpha = x$, we arrive at the cubic $x^3 + 2x^2 - 4 = 0$. Any rational root of this cubic would have to be an integer and, as a matter of fact, a divisor of 4. We find by direct substitution that none of these divisors satisfy the equation; thus *the cubic has no rational roots*, and, by the same token, has *no quadratic roots*. Hence, the crescent (4.1) is *nonquadrable*.

Type (4.3): Here $\gamma = \omega$, $\alpha = 3\omega$, $\beta = 4\omega$. The defining equation is $\sqrt{3}$ sin $4\gamma = 2$ sin 3γ. Proceeding as before, we arrive at an *irreducible cubic*, and conclude that the crescent (4.3) is *nonquadrable*.

Type (5.1): Here

$$\sin 5\alpha = \sqrt{5} \sin \alpha = 5 \sin \alpha - 20 \sin^3 \alpha + 16 \sin^5 \alpha.$$

We are thus led to the *biquadratic*

$$16x^4 - 20x^2 + (5 - \sqrt{5}) = 0.$$

We find

$$x = \sin \alpha = \tfrac{1}{2}\sqrt{\frac{5 - \sqrt{5 + 4\sqrt{5}}}{2}}.$$

Thus the crescent (5.1) is *quadrable*.

Type (5.3): Here $\alpha = 3\omega$, $\beta = 5\omega$, $\gamma = 2\omega$. The defining equation is: $\sqrt{3}$ sin $5\omega = \sqrt{5}$ sin 3ω. Like type (5.1), the latter leads to a quadratic in $\sin^2 \omega$. The crescent (5.3) is, therefore, *quadrable*.

Types (5.2) *and* (5.4) lead to *irreducible quartics* and are, therefore, *nonquadrable*.

The preceding discussion follows the lines of an essay published in 1840 by the German mathematician, Theodore Claussen, who, as far as I know, was the first to subject the Hippocratean problem to an algebraic analysis. His analysis, as we just saw, yielded not only the three quadrable crescents, (2.1), (3.1), (3.2), discovered by Hippocrates, but also the two crescents of "order" 5, namely, (5.1) and (5.3); it proved, moreover, that the remaining crescents of order 5 were nonquadrable, and that the same held for the crescents of orders 4 and 6. Claussen conjectured that *the Hippocratean problem had no other quadrable solutions than the five crescents just mentioned;* but that if any other crescents did exist, they would have to be of *prime order.*

This last hypothesis was vindicated when sixty-odd years later Edmund Landau proved that not only is the *order of a quadrable* crescent a prime number, but it must be a *Fermat prime,* i.e., of the form $2^n + 1$. Now, these primes play a very important part in *cyclotomy,* i.e., the division of a circle into equal parts. In more familiar terms, if it is possible to construct by straightedge and compass a regular polygon of an odd number of sides, say q, then q is either a Fermat prime, such as 3, 5, 17, 257, . . . , or a *square-free product of such primes.* Could it be that there was some recondite kinship between quadrable crescents and the regular polygons amenable to straightedge-compass constructions?

Well, long before speculations on this theme could gain momentum, it was found that *none of the 16 crescents of order 17 was quadrable.* The Claussen forecast was further strengthened when in 1934 the Russian mathematician Tchebotarev proved that the *crescent* (q, p) *is nonquadrable, if* p *is odd and* q *greater than* 5. Finally, in 1947, the Russian Dorodnov extended Tchebotarev's results to *even values of* p, thus confirming the remarkable conjecture which Claussen had made more than a hundred years earlier that *the only quadrable Hippocratean crescents were*

$$(2.1), (3.1), (3.2), (5.1) \text{ and } (5.3). \quad . \quad (10.12)$$

13

Such is the history of a problem which ranks among the earliest in the annals of mathematics. Formulated within one hundred and fifty years of the Founder's death and—which is even more significant—one hundred and fifty years before Euclid's *Elements* saw the light of day, it remained in a state of suspended animation for nearly twenty-four hundred years, and was only partly resolved after the combined resources of modern analysis and number theory were enlisted in its behalf.

I say *partly*, because the Claussen-Landau-Dorodnov theorems deal with the *algebraic* aspect of the problem only. There is still the question: Are the restrictions imposed by Hippocrates necessary conditions of quadrability? Specifically, the problem consists of determining values of α and β for which all three functions

$$\sin \alpha, \sin \beta, \text{ and } H = \beta \sin^2 \alpha - \alpha \sin^2 \beta \quad . \quad (10.13)$$

can be simultaneously expressed in terms of rational numbers and quadratic surds bearing on rational numbers; or of *proving that no such values exist*, unless $H = 0$. And this problem of *transcendental arithmetic* has, as far as I know, not even been tapped.

Chapter Eleven

THE QUADRATRIX OF HIPPIAS

It is one thing to execute a construction by tongue as it were, quite another to carry it out with instruments in hand.

JACOB STEINER

I

The Sophist, Hippias of Elis, a near-contemporary of Hippocrates of Chios, invented the curve for the express purpose of *squaring the circle*. A century or so later, the Hippian solution was restored and amplified by Dinostratus, a member of Plato's Academy and a brother of Menaechmus of *conic sections* fame. No written records of either the original or the restoration exist today. Pappus and other commentators have given a good description of the curve itself, but their explanations as to how the *quadratrix* was applied by Hippias and Dinostratus to the *quadrature* problem are far from satisfactory.

Some historians, misled by the term "mechanical" which earlier geometers used in describing the quadratrix, insinuate that Hippias relied on some sort of "mechanism" to generate the curve, forgetting that Greek mathematicians were wont to brand as mechanical any construction that implied loci other than lines and circles. Other historians, while recognizing the geometrical character of the approach, misinterpret the motivation, leaving the reader under the impression that Hippias and Dinostratus were merely begging the question.

2

The problem was *to construct a triangle the area of which was equal to that of a given circular sector*, specifically, a quadrant of a

138

circle. In Figure 23 the sector is $BOM = \frac{1}{2}Rs$, where R is the radius and s the length of the arc. Assume OP equal to s: then the triangle BOP is equiareal with the sector. Next, suppose that the perpendicular to OP meets the radius OM continued in Q: then, as M sweeps the circumference, the point Q generates the *Hippian quadratrix*. If the latter were fully traced, it could serve as a *templet* not only for *squaring any circular*

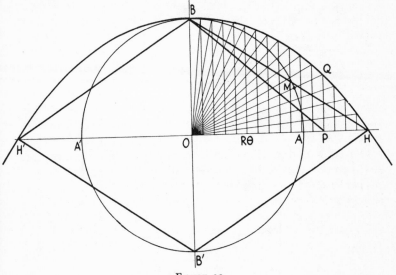

FIGURE 23

sector, but for *rectifying any circular arc*. In particular, the triangle HOB would be equiareal with the quadrant $OAMB$, and the rhombus $HBH'B'$ equiareal with the circle, and since the conversion of a rhombus into an equiareal square is a straight-edge-compass operation, the *squaring of the circle* would be effectively accomplished.

If the Hippian analysis ended here, the Sophist could be justly accused of begging the question. For, unless he knew how to rectify a circular arc, i.e., to erect a linear segment of equal length, he could not generate the quadratrix; and if he knew how to rectify a circular arc, then he would not need the quadratrix in the first place. However, it is a far more reasonable conjecture that, arrived at this point, Hippias *inverted* the problem, i.e., instead of seeking a rectilinear segment of length equal to a quadrant of a given circumference, he sought to *determine a circle, one quadrant of which was equal to a given rectilinear segment.* This meant to construct a quadratrix of given base, a task which could be effected point by point without stepping out of the traditional domain.

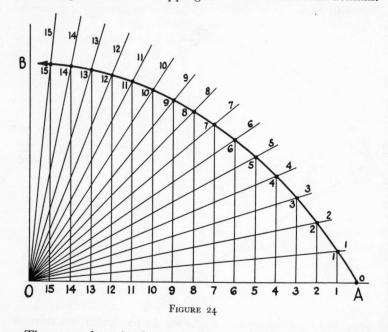

FIGURE 24

The procedure is shown in Figure 24. A set of equally spaced rays divide the right angle *XOY* into *n* equal angles; the given segment *OH* is divided in the same number, *n*, of equal parts. The perpendiculars to *OX* at the points of division meet the corresponding rays in points which lie on the quadratrix sought. By carrying the *dichotomy* far enough, the set of points may be rendered as *compact* as one wishes. As to the *vertex, B,* of the quadratrix, the goal of the Hippian problem, it cannot be reached directly by the operation at hand: it should be viewed as the *limit of an infinite dichotomy,* and this, I conjecture, was what Hippias actually had in mind.

3

According to this interpretation, the Hippian quadrature was an attempt to define the ratio of a circumference of a circle to its diameter as a *limit of an infinite process*. The analytical counterpart to this graphical procedure is the formula

$$\text{Limit } n \tan \frac{\pi}{2n} = \frac{\pi}{2} \qquad . \qquad . \qquad (\text{II.I})$$
$$n \to \infty$$

This, incidentally, was one of the formulae which Archimedes, two centuries later, used in determining rational approximations to π. In the Archimedean approach, the circle was viewed as the common limit of two series of regular polygons of which one was inscribed and the other circumscribed to the circle, the number of sides growing indefinitely. When applied to a quadrant of a circle, this approach leads to the inequality,

$$n \sin \frac{\pi}{2n} < \frac{\pi}{2} < n \tan \frac{\pi}{2n} \qquad . \qquad . \qquad (\text{II.2})$$

To appraise the ideas of Hippias one should remember that his quadrature was the first recorded venture into the field of *infinite processes*; that this venture took place about 450 B.C., at a time when mathematics was barely more than a century and a half old; that the Hippian *quadratrix* was the first curve (other than the circle, of course) of which we have any historical record; that this occurred at least a century before the discovery of *conic sections*; and that in his treatment of the curve Hippias employed devices which two thousand years later were turned by Fermat and Descartes into the basic implements of *analytic geometry*.

4

At this juncture I must give a brief outline of an issue which is a settled matter today, but had quite an eventful history in the past three centuries; namely, the *classification of plane*

curves. Greek efforts in this direction, based on strictly geometrical considerations, were rather superficial and, in a
sense, sterile. With the advent of analytic geometry, the
question entered a new phase.

Descartes was the first to propose that curves be classified
according to the character of their equations, i.e., of the
functional relations which represented them in a system of
rectilinear coordinates. He was particularly interested in loci the
equations of which could be put in the form of a *polynomial*
in two variables. Today, we call such loci *algebraic,* and define
as order of the curve the *degree, n,* of the representative polynomial. Descartes, however, had different ideas on this subject: he defined the order of a locus by the integers $\frac{1}{2}n$ or
$\frac{1}{2}(n + 1)$, depending on whether n was *even* or *odd.* Thus, what
we designate today as *cubics* and *quartics* were to Descartes
curves of the second order, while *straight lines* and *conics* were
defined as loci of the first order.

Newton did identify the order of a locus with the degree of
its equation, but not without reservations. His reluctance to
class straight lines among curves led him to define the integer
$n - 1$ as the *genus* of the locus. Thus the straight line was
catalogued *as locus of order* 1 *and genus* 0. In spite of Newton's
prestige, the idea did not take root, and today the term genus
is used in an entirely different sense.

As to such curves as *cycloids, spirals* and *sinusoids,* which we
catalogue today as *transcendental,* there is no record that Newton
had a collective name for this non-algebraic variety. He did
state, however, that the order of such loci should be viewed as
infinity, inasmuch as a straight line may intersect such a curve
in an infinite number of points.

5

The term *transcendental* was coined by Leibnitz. This mystic
philosopher-mathematician was endowed with an extraordinary intuition and foresight. He anticipated many a
mathematical trend, sometimes as much as a century before
it reached the stage of fruition. The division of numbers and

functions into *algebraic*, or, as Leibnitz called them, *analytic* and *transcendental*, is a case in point. As though foreshadowing the course of modern algebra, Leibnitz stated, in so many words, that to every algebraic number there may be assigned one and only one algebraic equation with rational coefficients. The degree of this equation he calls the *order* of the algebraic number. Recognizing, however, that magnitudes exist to which no polynomial can be assigned, he proposed to call these *transcendental* because, as he put it, they *transcend algebraic analysis*.

In a similar manner, functions exist which cannot be transformed into polynomial relations no matter how many rational manipulations may be undertaken to that end. These functions Leibnitz defined as *transcendental*. He was frankly puzzled by the fact that a transcendental equation may admit of an algebraic and even of a rational solution, as, for example, the equation $x^x + x = 30$, which is satisfied by the integer $x = 3$. However, he viewed such "phenomena" as exceptions, maintaining that, "on the whole," *transcendental equations are satisfied by transcendental numbers only*.

The subsequent course of events has justified Leibnitz' perplexity, and has strengthened, at the same time, the plausibility of his conjecture. The relation between transcendental numbers on the one hand and transcendental functions on the other persists as an unsolved problem to this day. The histories of the Hippocratean crescents, of the *transcendence* of the numbers e and π, and the many pending questions of *transcendental arithmetic* foreshadow that the Leibnitz problem will remain on mathematical agenda for some time to come.

6

Our textbooks on analytic geometry follow methodically the classification just outlined. After disposing of the straight line and the circle, they take up the conic sections, or curves of the second order. This is followed by cubics and quartics, and algebraic curves generally. The study of transcendental curves is relegated to the end of the course, and, in some curricula, postponed until the student has acquired some rudiments of the calculus.

Now, all this is as it should be. Having put algebra into the foreground of mathematical instruction, we must needs begin with rational and finite operations; and this predicates the order of exposition, whether the subject be number, function or graph. And yet, in all fairness to the more sophisticated student, we should inform him that historical sequence has not always agreed with the order of exposition of a textbook.

The Hippian quadratrix is a case in point. Choose the base of the curve and its axis of symmetry for reference frame, and the radius of the generating circle for unit of length. Then, by definition, arc $\overline{BM} = \overline{OP} = x$; again, if we agree to measure angles in radians, then agle BOQ is also equal to x, and the right triangle POQ yields the relation:

$$y = x \cot x \qquad . \qquad . \qquad . \qquad (11.3)$$

This is the equation of the curve in rectangular coordinates, and inasmuch as *cot* x *cannot be represented as a polynomial in* x, *the quadratrix is a transcendental curve.*

Thus, after the straight line and the circle, *the first locus studied by mathematicians was a transcendental curve,* while even such simple algebraic curves as the conic sections did not emerge on the mathematical scene until a century and a half later. Truly, history is no respecter of systems.

Chapter Twelve

THE ALGORITHM OF EUCLID

Magnitudes are said to have a ratio to one another
when the lesser can be multiplied so as to exceed
the greater.

EUCLID, Book V

I

Book Seven of the *Elements* contains the description of a
numerical device which has come to be known as *Euclidean
algorithm*, although it probably antedates Euclid by at least
one hundred years. Euclid applies the algorithm to determining the *greatest divisor common to two integers*. To illustrate,
take the numbers 2,601 and 1,088; a chain of successive
divisions leads to the identities:

$$
\begin{aligned}
2{,}601 &= 2 \times 1{,}088 + 425 \\
1{,}088 &= 2 \times 425 + 238 \\
425 &= 1 \times 238 + 187 \\
238 &= 1 \times 187 + 51 \\
187 &= 3 \times 51 + 34 \\
51 &= 1 \times 34 + 17 \\
34 &= 2 \times 17
\end{aligned}
$$

The last *residue*, 17, is the greatest common divisor sought,
because any divisor common to 2,601 and 1,088 must also
divide the remainder 425, and, by the same token, must
divide 238, 187, 51, 34 and 17.

When the same algorithm is applied to two *relatively prime
integers*, A and B, it results in the expansion of A/B into a
regular continued fraction. I shall illustrate this in the case of
41/16:

$$
\begin{aligned}
41 &= 16 \times 2 + 9 \quad &\text{or} \quad 41/16 &= 2 + 9/16 \\
16 &= 9 \times 1 + 7 \quad &\text{or} \quad 16/9 &= 1 + 7/9 \\
9 &= 7 \times 1 + 2 \quad &\text{or} \quad 9/7 &= 1 + 2/7 \\
7 &= 2 \times 3 + 1 \quad &\text{or} \quad 7/2 &= 3 + 1/2
\end{aligned}
$$

Hence the expansion:

$$\frac{41}{16} = 2 + \cfrac{1}{1 + \cfrac{1}{1 + \cfrac{1}{3 + \cfrac{1}{2}}}}$$

Observe that the *quotients* generated by the algorithm become the terms of the expansion. Since the continued fraction is completely determined by these quotients, we may write without ambiguity: $41/16 = (2; 1, 1, 3, 2)$.

It is obvious enough that the procedure exhibited on this example applies to any two integers. Thus any rational number may be expanded into a terminating continued fraction, and *the expansion is unique.* By the same token, any rational number can be represented by a finite array of positive integers. In what follows I shall call that array the *spectrum* of the number.

2

The expansion into continued fraction, the Euclidean algorithm and the spectrum to which it gives rise are susceptible of a striking graphical representation which is exhibited in Figure 25 in the case of $41/16$, the example treated above. In the graph, the numerator and denominator of the fraction are interpreted as sides of a rectangle. From this rectangle we remove as many squares as possible, leaving a *residual* rectangle to which the algorithm is applied anew, and the process is continued *until no residual rectangle remains.* The number of squares in each "tier" gives the corresponding element of the spectrum, i.e., a term of the continued fraction.

I said that *to any rational number corresponds a unique spectrum.* Conversely, *any ordered array of positive integers may be construed as the spectrum of some rational number.* To calculate the latter, one could express the spectrum as a continued fraction and then reverse the Euclidean algorithm. A far more effective method was discovered by John Wallis. The *Wallis algorithm* is exhibited in the following table for the spectrum $(2; 1, 1, 3, 2)$.

Terms of Spectrum	2	1	1	3	2
Numerators of Convergents	2	3	3×1+2=5	5×3+3=18	18×2+5=41
Denominators of Convergents	1	1	1×1+1=2	2×3+1= 7	7×2+2=16

The successive *convergents* are the values of the "curtailed" spectra, the last convergent being the value of the continued fraction. Thus, the convergents of 41/16 are

$$\frac{2}{1}, \frac{3}{1}, \frac{5}{2}, \frac{18}{7} \text{ and } \frac{41}{16}.$$

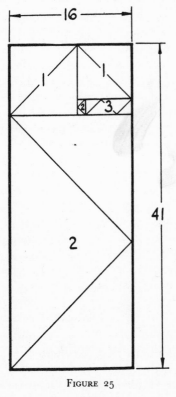

FIGURE 25

147

3

The theoretical importance of the Wallis algorithm is that it opens the way to a rigorous treatment of *infinite continued fractions*. To be sure, such infinite processes were used long before Wallis: explicitly, by the Italian mathematicians of the sixteenth century; implicitly, by Fibonacci, Hero and Archimedes. However, Wallis, and later Huygens, put the theory on a solid basis by establishing that *the process was convergent for any infinite spectrum*, i.e., that the *sequence of convergents always approached a limit*. This limit is *necessarily irrational, since the spectrum of any rational number is necessarily finite*.

We conclude that any array of positive integers, finite or infinite, may be interpreted as the spectrum of some *real* number Γ: *if the spectrum is finite, Γ is rational; if the spectrum is infinite, Γ is irrational*. Conversely, any positive number Γ, rational or irrational, may be expanded into a continued fraction: *the expansion is finite, if Γ is rational; infinite, if Γ is irrational*. Furthermore, the individual steps in the expansion of an irrational number into a continued fraction follow the pattern of the Euclidean algorithm, and *the infinite algorithm may*, accordingly, *be viewed as a direct generalization of the finite*.

4

The *generic operation* of this extended algorithm can be expressed in very simple terms, by introducing the symbol $[\Gamma]$ to denote *the greatest integer contained in the positive number* Γ. Discard the trivial case when $\cdot\Gamma$ is an integer; then, the difference $\Gamma - [\Gamma]$ is contained between 0 and 1, which means that there always exists a number X greater than 1 such that

$$\Gamma = [\Gamma] + \frac{1}{X}. \qquad . \qquad . \qquad (12.1)$$

If Γ is a rational number, say A/B, then $[\Gamma]$ is the quotient in the division of A by B, and the operation is but a paraphrase of a step in Euclid's algorithm. If, however, Γ is irrational, then X, too, is irrational. Operating on X as we did on Γ, we obtain $X = [X] + 1/Y$, where Y, too, is an irrational number greater than 1. The process will, therefore, continue indefinitely, generating an *infinite sequence of positive integers*

$$[\Gamma], [X], [Y], [Z], \ldots \qquad \cdot \qquad \cdot \qquad (12.2)$$

These are *the denominators of the infinite continued fraction which tends to the irrational Γ as limit.*

5

The Dutch mathematician Huygens is credited with being the first to use continued fractions as a means of deriving *rational approximations*. The effectiveness of the method rests on two properties of the Euclidean algorithm which may be formulated as follows:

I. If A/B and A'/B' are two consecutive convergents in the expansion of the number Γ, then Γ *is contained between A/B and A'/B'*. Thus, we shall see in the sequel, that $265/153$ and $362/209$ are the ninth and tenth convergents respectively in the expansion of $\sqrt{3}$, which means that

$$\frac{265}{153} < \sqrt{3} < \frac{362}{209}$$

II. If A/B is a convergent in the expansion of Γ, then the *error* committed in writing A/B for Γ is less than $1/B^2$. Thus, by taking $362/209$ for $\sqrt{3}$ we are approximating the latter within an error less than $1/40{,}000$. As a matter of fact, comparing the fraction with the tabular value of $\sqrt{3}$, we find:

$$\sqrt{3} = 1 \cdot 732051 \ldots , \quad 362/209 = 1 \cdot 732052 \ldots$$

Unfortunately, the effectiveness of the method is largely vitiated by the tedious work involved in determining the spectrum of the irrational. In this respect, the irrationals of the type $M + \sqrt{N}$, where M and N are rational numbers, are in a class by themselves, in that the pattern of the spectrum can to some extent be predicted beforehand, as may be seen from the following examples.

6

First example; the *golden section* ratio. The reciprocal of the "divine proportion" is $\Gamma = \frac{1}{2}(\sqrt{5} + 1)$. (See Chapter Five.) We find $[\Gamma] = 1$ and $\Gamma - [\Gamma] = \frac{1}{2}(\sqrt{5} - 1)$. The reciprocal of this is $X = \frac{1}{2}(\sqrt{5} + 1)$; thus $X = \Gamma$ and $[X] = 1$. Hence

$$\frac{1}{2}(\sqrt{5} + 1) = (1; 1, 1, 1, \ldots). \qquad . \qquad (12.3)$$

The Wallis algorithm yields here a so-called *Fibonacci sequence*:

$$1, 2, 3, 5, 8, 13, 21, 34, \ldots, \qquad . \qquad (12.4)$$

where *any term beginning with the third is the sum of the two terms which precede it.*

Second example. Let us seek the expansion of the quadratic surd $\Gamma = \sqrt{3}$, which will play an important part in the discussion of the Archimedean approximation. We find here $\Gamma - [\Gamma] = \sqrt{3} - 1$, the reciprocal of which is $X = \frac{1}{2}(\sqrt{3} + 1)$. Hence, $X - (X) = \frac{1}{2}(\sqrt{3} - 1)$, $Y = \sqrt{3} + 1$. Thus,

$$[Y] = 2, \quad Y - [Y] = \sqrt{3} - 1.$$

The reciprocal of the latter is $\frac{1}{2}(\sqrt{3} + 1)$, i.e., X, and we conclude that

$$\sqrt{3} = (1 : 1,2, 1,2, 1,2, \ldots). \qquad . \qquad (12.5)$$

Third example. Set $\Gamma = \sqrt{19}$. The procedure is the same as in the preceding examples. I leave the details to the reader. The result is:

$$\sqrt{19} = (4; 2,1,3,1,2,8, 2,1,3,1,2,8, 2,1,3,1,2,8, \ldots) \qquad . \qquad (12.6)$$

7

The expansions in the preceding examples have one feature in common: each contains an *infinite number of identical blocks of terms.* Such continued fractions are known as *periodic*; the recurrent block is called the *cycle*, and the number of terms in a cycle the *period* of the expansion. Thus, for example, in the expansion of $\sqrt{19}$ the cycle is 2,1,3,1,2,8 and the period is 6.

The very procedure used in deriving these expansions suggests that, when applied to irrationals of type $M + \sqrt{N}$, the Euclidean algorithm will invariably generate a *periodic spectrum*, and such is indeed the case: *the spectrum of any irrational of the form* $M + \sqrt{N}$, *where M and N are rational numbers, is necessarily periodic;* conversely, *the limit of any periodic continued fraction is a root of some quadratic equation with rational coefficients*, i.e., an irrational *of the binomial type* $M + \sqrt{N}$.

There is a remarkable analogy between *periodic continued fractions* and *periodic decimal fractions*. If Γ is a positive rational number, i.e., the root of a *linear equation* with rational coefficients, then the decimal fraction which represents Γ is either *terminating* or *periodic*. Similarly if Γ is a positive root of a *quadratic equation* with rational coefficients, then the continued fraction which represents Γ is either *terminating* or *periodic*. In the linear case the generating process is *long division*, in the quadratic it is *Euclid's algorithm*.

These periodic properties of quadratic irrationals were known to Huygens, Wallis and even to Bombelli, the Italian mathematician of the sixteenth century who was the first to use continued fractions explicitly. Euler and Lagrange not only provided these theorems with rigorous proofs, but showed how periodic continued fractions may be used to attack some difficult number-theoretical questions. The field was vastly extended by Legendre, Gauss, Jacobi, Galois and Liouville, among many others, until today a comprehensive exposition of the theory would require many a volume. With all that, quite a few questions propounded by these masters remain unanswered. Chief among these is the relation between the *character of an integer N* and the *period* and *cycle* of the spectrum of $\sqrt{N}$.

Chapter Thirteen

AN ARCHIMEDEAN APPROXIMATION

> Indeed, even more important than safeguarding truth is the preservation of the methods which have led to its discovery.
>
> PONCELET

I

In a tract entitled *Cyclometry*, Archimedes made use of the inequality

$$\frac{265}{153} < \sqrt{3} < \frac{1{,}351}{780}. \qquad \cdot \quad \cdot \qquad (13.1)$$

Both fractions are excellent approximations to $\sqrt{3}$, and it was this precision that had enabled the master-calculator to evaluate the ratio, π, of the circumference of a circle to its diameter within the narrow limits:

$$3\frac{10}{71} < \pi < 3\frac{10}{70}. \qquad \cdot \quad \cdot \qquad (13.2)$$

Archimedes described in detail the successive steps in his evaluation, but gave no inkling as to how he had arrived at the approximations to $\sqrt{3}$ which had served as his point of departure. Could it be that these values were such common knowledge among the geometers to whom the tract was addressed that he viewed such elaborations as redundant? Perhaps! Still, speculations have been rife ever since as to the motives which had governed the Archimedean choice.

Both approximations are *convergents* into a continued fraction for $\sqrt{3}$, and so it is natural to suspect that it was the Euclidean algorithm that had led to these values. However, this conjecture has been contested by historians on the ground that continued fractions were not introduced until the sixteenth century, that the theory did not come to full fruition until the eighteenth, and that it was, therefore, entirely outside the ken of Greek mathematics. This last statement deserves closer scrutiny.

2

We know that the Euclidean algorithm was born on Greek soil, that there is nothing in its definition or execution which would restrict it to rational numbers, and that men like Eudoxus, Euclid and Archimedes could not have failed to recognize in it an ideal *criterion of commensurability* of two magnitudes. I would not go so far as to assert that the algorithm was invented for the express purpose of defining irrationals, but it is not unlikely that whoever discovered the process was at the time in quest of such criteria of commensurability. To be sure, no documentary evidence exists to substantiate this conjecture; but then one should remember that Greek geometers studiously avoided the use of such terms as *infinite* or *limit*.

A case in point is the Archimedean theorem on *the area of a parabolic segment*, the proof of which depends on the summation of the *infinite geometric progression*

$$1 + \frac{1}{4} + \frac{1}{4^2} + \frac{1}{4^3} + \ldots$$

At no time did Archimedes state that the sum of the progression approached 4/3 as a *limit*, or words to that effect; he merely maintained that no matter how many terms were taken, their sum would never exceed 4/3.

It has also been contended by some historians that even if some Greek mathematician had envisaged the possibility of applying the Euclidean algorithm to quadratic surds, he would have lacked the requisite technique to implement it. This argument, too, is unfounded. Indeed, Book Ten of Euclid's *Elements* presents a comprehensive theory of binomials of type $A + \sqrt{B}$, including all the operations necessary for the expansion of such irrationals into continued fractions.

3

However, there is one aspect of the Archimedean approximation that casts reasonable doubt on the continued fraction conjecture. We saw in the preceding chapter that the expansion of $\sqrt{3}$ leads to the *periodic spectrum* $(1; 1,2, 1,2, \dots)$. The The first twelve convergents of this expansion are:

$$F_1 = 1 \quad F_4 = \frac{7}{4} \quad F_7 = \frac{71}{41} \quad F_{10} = \frac{362}{209}$$

$$F_2 = 2 \quad F_5 = \frac{19}{11} \quad F_8 = \frac{97}{56} \quad F_{11} = \frac{989}{571} \quad \Bigg\} \quad . \quad (13 \cdot 3)$$

$$F_3 = \frac{5}{3} \quad F_6 = \frac{26}{15} \quad F_9 = \frac{265}{153} \quad F_{12} = \frac{1,351}{780}$$

Observe that while the two fractions which enter in inequality (13.1) are among these convergents, *they are not consecutive convergents*. To determine F_{12} by the Euclidean algorithm one would have to calculate F_{11} first. But if Archimedes had F_{11} at hand, why did he not use it to obtain the "sharper" inequality:

$$\frac{989}{571} < \sqrt{3} < \frac{1,351}{780}?$$

4

A passage from Hero's book *Metrica* offers a clue to this riddle. This work contains, among other valuable historical material, the celebrated *area formula*, which is the theme of the next chapter. The application of this formula requires, generally, the approximate *evaluation of a square root*, and so Hero takes time out to instruct his readers how to perform such an operation "with accuracy and dispatch." The Heronian algorithm is a precedure which one would class today as *successive linear interpolations*. While Hero used it for the extraction of square and cube roots, the method is far more general, and, as a matter of fact, can be successfully applied to the solution of the equation F $(x) = 0$, where F (x) is any *single-valued rational function*.

In Figure 26, the curve (F) is the graph of the function $y = $ F (x). The abscissa a of the "pole" A is some rational number "reasonably" close to the true value of the root x; b is

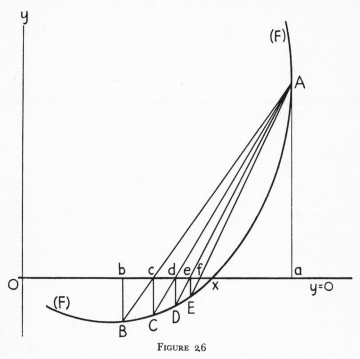

FIGURE 26

another such rational number, and B the corresponding point on the curve (F). The line $A B$ meets the x-axis in a point of abscissa c: the crux of the principle is that *c is a better rational approximation to x than either a or b*. By performing the same operation on C, we generate a rational number d which approximates the irrational x even better than c. It follows that by repeated application of the algorithm we may approach the root x with any desired precision, the *rapidity of the convergence* depending largely on the choice of the pole A.

5

For the evaluation of $\sqrt{R}$, the algorithm leads to the iteration formula

$$u_{n+1} = \frac{au_n + R}{u_n + a} \qquad . \qquad . \qquad (13.5)$$

As an illustration, consider the example treated in the *Metrica:* $\sqrt{720} = 12\sqrt{5}$. Set $a = 2$: then

$$u_{n+1} = \frac{2u_n + 5}{u_n + 2}$$

With the initial value $u_1 = a = 2$, we arrive at the set

$$u_1 = 2, \; u_2 = \frac{9}{4}, \; u_3 = \frac{38}{17}, \; u_4 = \frac{161}{72},$$

and the last term yields for $\sqrt{720}$ the approximation $161/6$, which is the result given by Hero.

The extraction of $\sqrt[3]{R}$ leads to the iteration formula

$$u_n{}^+{}_1 = \frac{au_n{}^2 + a^2u_n + R}{u_n{}^2 + au_n + a^2} \qquad . \qquad . \qquad (13.6)$$

As an example, let us evaluate $\sqrt[3]{10}$. Here $R = 10$, and we take for a the greatest integer contained in $\sqrt[3]{10}$ Thus

$$u_{n+1} = \frac{2u_n{}^2 + 4u_n + 10}{u_n{}^2 + 2u_n + 4} \qquad . \qquad . \qquad (13.7)$$

Set $u_1 = a = 2$: then $u_2 = 13/6$ and $u_3 = 1010/469$, which deviates from the *tabular* value of $\sqrt[3]{10}$, 2.1536, by less than .0001.

6

Let us now return to the Heronian technique for the extraction of square roots and examine how it works out in the case of $\sqrt{3}$. To this end, set in formula (13.5) $R = 3$ and denote by u_n and u_{n+1} any two consecutive terms in the iteration process; the result is the relation:

$$u_{n+1} = \frac{au_n + 3}{u_n + a} \qquad \cdot \qquad \cdot \qquad (13.8)$$

As I said before, the sequence will converge to $\sqrt{3}$ for any reasonable choice of the *initial value*, G. It is obvious, however, that the choice of the *operator* G will have a decided influence on the rapidity of the convergence. For reasons, on which I shall not speculate here, Hero chose $a = 5/3$. This leads to the formula,

$$u_{n+1} = \frac{5u_n + 9}{3u_n + 5} \qquad \cdot \qquad \cdot \qquad (13.9)$$

and to a sequence, the first four terms of which are the fractions

$$\frac{5}{3}, \frac{26}{15}, \frac{265}{153}, \frac{1{,}351}{780}. \qquad \cdot \qquad \cdot \qquad (13.10)$$

Now, the last two are precisely those which enter in the *Archimedean inequality for* $\sqrt{3}$. Was this coincidence accidental? Hardly! To be sure, in describing his procedure, Hero makes no reference to Archimedes or to any earlier sources for that matter. And yet, it is utterly inconceivable that a brilliant scholar who had full access to the Alexandrian Library would be unfamiliar with such an important work as *Cyclometry*. It is far more probable that the technique described in *Metrica* was not a Heronian discovery, but was known to Archimedes and even to his predecessors.

Indeed, the ideas back of the procedure are fully within the ken of classical mathematics. Thus, the individual steps in the process are based on *linear interpolation*, which, after all, is the most natural approach to the technique of approximation. As to the process itself, one makes a "reasonably good guess" and iterates the guess on the theory that the result is closer to the true solution than the original value. The scheme was widely practised in classical days, and was described in Latin textbooks on mathematics as *regula falsi*.

The four Heronian approximates to $\sqrt{3}$ listed in (13.10) are all *convergents* in the expansion of $\sqrt{3}$ into a continued fraction. What is more, it can be shown that *the infinite sequence generated by the iteration* (13.9) *is made up entirely of such convergents*. In fact, if we denote, as before, by F_n the convergent of *rank n*, the terms of the infinite sequence can be expressed as

$$F_3, \ F_6, \ F_9, \ F_{12}, \ \ldots F_{3p}, \ \ldots \qquad . \qquad (13.11)$$

When viewed in this light, the Heronian algorithm appears as a sort of a "hop-skip" scheme, the net effect of which is the speeding up of the Euclidean algorithm. And this is not all: the iteration used by Hero is but a special application of a general property contained in the relation

$$H(F_m, F_n) = \frac{F_m F_n + 3}{F_m + F_n} = F_{m+n} \qquad (13.12)$$

To illustrate, consider F_{12}. In virtue of (13.12) we can evaluate this convergent in several ways. Thus

(A) $\ F_{12} = H(F_5, F_7) = \dfrac{19 \times 71 + 3 \times 11 \times 41}{19 \times 41 + 11 \times 71} = \dfrac{2{,}702}{1{,}560}$
$$= \frac{1{,}351}{780}$$

(B) $\ F_{12} = H(F_6, F_6) = \dfrac{26 \times 26 + 3 \times 15 \times 15}{2 \times 15 \times 26} = \dfrac{1{,}351}{780}$

(C) $\ F_{12} = H(F_4, F_8) = \dfrac{7 \times 97 + 3 \times 4 \times 56}{7 \times 56 + 4 \times 97} = \dfrac{1{,}351}{780}$

Furthermore, we can derive the 24th convergent from the 12th without intermediate steps, since

$$F_{24} = \frac{F_{12}^2 + 3}{2 . F_{12}} = \frac{1{,}351^2 + 3 \cdot 780^2}{2 . 1{,}351 . 780}$$

The denominator of this convergent is of the order of 10^6; it follows that the fraction approximates $\sqrt{3}$ within an error less than 10^{-12}.

8

The remarkable kinship between the Euclidean and Heronian algorithms is a consequence of a theorem on *periodic continued fractions* due to Lagrange. The proof of this fundamental proposition is beyond the scope of this volume. I shall add, however, for the sake of completeness, that the Lagrangian theory covers the most general surd of type $\sqrt{R}$, where R is a positive integer. As a result, the relationship between the two algorithms can also be extended to the most general surd of that type. Indeed, even the outward form of this kinship is retained. For, within some reservations on which I shall not insist here, the formula

$$H(F_m, F_n) = \frac{F_m F_n + R}{F_m + F_n} = F_{m+n} \qquad . \qquad (13.13)$$

remains valid for the *convergents of* the general surd $\sqrt{R}$.

The Lagrangian memoir on the subject appeared about 1775. Thus more than two thousand years separate the two episodes of the story I have told here. The arguments and technique used by Lagrange in establishing his theory, and the consequent kinship between the two procedures, involve considerations of algebra and number theory which were altogether outside the ken of Greek mathematicians. Granted that the alleged calculating technique which had led to the inequality did not transcend their mathematical knowledge, there still remains the perplexing question as to what governed their choice of the *initial value*, 5/3.

Chapter Fourteen

THE FORMULA OF HERO

The mathematician is like a Frenchman: you tell him
something, he translates it into his own language,
and at once it becomes something altogether different.

GOETHE

I

We know as little about the life of Hero as we do of Euclid's
life; in fact, less. For, while we can definitely place the
Elements about 300 B.C., all we can say about Hero is that he
flourished in Alexandria during the first century. Unfortunately,
there were two first centuries, and the question whether his
activities belong to B.C. or A.D. has not been settled to date.
Of one thing we are certain: Hero's *Metrica* and *Dioptra* ante-
date the *Almagest* of Ptolemy, who flourished about A.D. 150.

The celebrated Heronian formula is usually presented in
the form

$$T = \sqrt{s(s-a)(s-b)(s-c)} \qquad . \qquad (14.1)$$

where a, b, c are the *sides*, T is the *area* of the triangle and
$s = \frac{1}{2}(a+b+c)$ the *semiperimeter*. To prove his theorem Hero
takes the triangle $a = 7$, $b = 8$, $c = 9$. Here, $s = 12$,
$s - a = 5$, $s - b = 4$, $s - c = 3$. Hence $T = \sqrt{720}$, which
Hero evaluates by the method described in the preceding
chapter.

The most natural approach to establishing the formula is
to start with the theorem that the area of a triangle is *one
half of the product of base and altitude*, and this is how most textbooks proceed. To calculate the altitude, the Pythagorean
theorem is applied, which brings in the segments of the base,
and these are later eliminated by rather complicated algebraic
manipulations. Such a proof is usually accompanied by the
apology that it is not difficult, just involved. But elementary

as this approach may appear to us today, it was entirely beyond the ken of the Heronian period.

2

In the Heronian proof, the auxiliary element is not an altitude of the triangle but *the radius of the inscribed circle*. In Figure 27 the centre J of the inscribed circle is joined to the vertices A, B, C. The three triangles BJC, CJA, AJB have areas

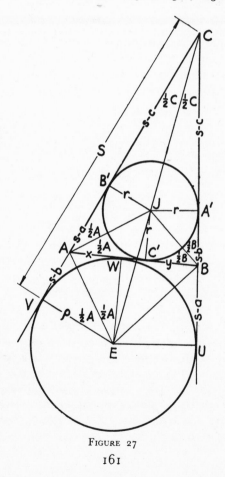

FIGURE 27

$\frac{1}{2}ra$, $\frac{1}{2}rb$, $\frac{1}{2}rc$, respectively, where r is the radius of the inscribed circle. Hence

$$T = \tfrac{1}{2}r(a + b + c) = rs. \qquad \qquad (14.2)$$

Thus, the problem is reduced to expressing r in terms of a, b, c.

To this end, Hero introduces an *escribed circle*, which touches the sides CA and CB on the outside, and the side AB between A and B. He then proceeds to evaluate—and this is the crux of his proof—the *tangential segments*, in terms of the sides. It is easily shown that

$$AV = AW = s - a, \quad BW = BU = s - b,$$
$$CU = CV = s - c, \quad AV' = s - b, \quad CV' = s.$$

Once this is established, the rest is a matter of similar triangles. The centres J and E being on the bisector of the angle C, the triangles JVC and $EV'C$ are similar: hence, if we denote the radius of the escribed circle by ρ, we have

$$\rho : r = (s - c) : s.$$

On the other hand, JAE is a right angle, and, consequently, the right triangles JVA and $EV'A$ are also similar, i.e.,

$$r : (s - a) = (s - b) : \rho.$$

Eliminating ρ between these two relations, we arrive at

$$r^2 = \frac{(s - a)(s - b)(s - c)}{s}; \qquad \qquad (14.3)$$

and combining this with (14.2), we obtain the *Heronian formula*.

3

Hero illustrates the method on a score of examples. In each case the sides of the triangle are integers. He is fully aware that *the area of such a rational triangle is generally an irrational number*. However, he states without proof the existence of an infinitude of triangles with rational areas as well as sides. Today we call such triangles *Heronian triples*. Any Pythagorean triple is obviously Heronian, since $T = \frac{1}{2}ab$. We shall presently see that by a proper combination of two Pythagorean triples one can generate at least one Heronian triple.

The construction is shown in Figure 28, where ABC and $A'B'C'$ are two Pythagorean triangles, and ZX and ZY are parallel to AB and $A'B'$, respectively. Let us take for $h = OZ$

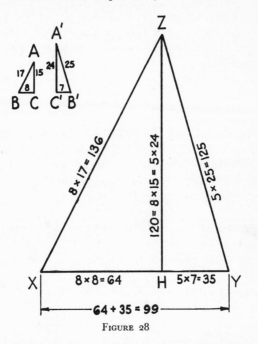

FIGURE 28

the least common multiple of the integers b *and* b′: we can then write $h = Nb = N'b'$, where N and N' are relatively prime. From similar triangles we deduce the sides of XYZ as

$$x = N'c', \; y = Nc, \; z = Na + N'a'. \qquad (14.4)$$

The *triangle is Heronian*, because its area $T = \frac{1}{2}hz$ is a rational number. In Figure 31 the Pythagorean triples are (8, 15; 17) and (7, 24; 25) and the reader will verify that the resulting Heronian triple is (125, 136, 99).

4

A far more elegant solution to the Heronian problem was given by Brahmagupta, a Hindu mathematician of the seventh century A.D. He takes for *parameters* the ratios, α, β, γ, defined by

$$\alpha = \frac{s-a}{r} = \cot \tfrac{1}{2}A, \ \beta = \frac{s-b}{r} = \cot \tfrac{1}{2}B,$$

$$\gamma = \frac{s-c}{r} = \cot \tfrac{1}{2}C.$$

. . (14.5)

Assuming that A and B are the acute angles of the triangle, the parameters α and β are greater than 1; as to γ, it is greater, equal or less than 1, depending on whether C is acute, right or obtuse. On the other hand, α, β, γ are not independent of each other. They are connected by the relation:

$$\alpha\beta\gamma = \alpha + \beta + \gamma \ \text{or} \ \gamma = \frac{\alpha+\beta}{\alpha\beta-1}, \ . \quad (14.6)$$

which reduces the problem to *two degrees of freedom*.

5

These considerations are valid for any triangle; but in the case of a Heronian triple, *the radius* r *is rational*, and, consequently, *the parameters* α, β, γ *are rational numbers*. Conversely, if *the sum of three rational numbers is equal to their product*, and two of these numbers are greater than 1, then they can be taken as *Brahmagupta parameters of a Heronian triple*. As a matter of fact, in so far as form alone is concerned, the triple is completely defined by the proportion

$$\frac{a}{\beta+\gamma} = \frac{b}{\gamma+\alpha} = \frac{c}{\alpha+\beta}. \quad . \quad (14.7)$$

To illustrate, take $\alpha = 2$, $\beta = 7/4$. We find $\gamma = 3/2$. Bringing these to a common denominator and dropping the latter, we are led to the integers 8, 7, 6. Hence the triple $(7 + 6, 6 + 8, 8 + 7)$, i.e., $(13, 14, 15)$. As another example take $\alpha = 3$, $\beta = 7$; then $\gamma = \frac{1}{2}$, which means that the angle C is obtuse; proceeding as before, we find the integers 6, 14, 1 which lead to the triple $(15, 7, 20)$.

The elegance of the Brahmagupta approach is further accentuated by the fact that the aggregate of *Pythagorean triples* is included under $\gamma = 1$. Indeed, if we set $\alpha = p/q$, then β has the value $(p + q)/(p - q)$; and equations (14.7) lead to

$$\frac{a}{2pq} = \frac{b}{p^2 - q^2} = \frac{c}{p^2 + q^2} \quad . \qquad (14.8)$$

It follows that p and q are the *Fibonacci* parameters of the Pythagorean triple. (See formula (9.7) of Chapter Nine.)

6

Among the Heronian triples treated in *Metrica* was the set of consecutive integers $(13, 14, 15)$. Hero found other such "consecutive" triples, and, probably, surmised that their number was infinite. However, he failed to devise a systematic procedure for generating such triples. Nor did the Hindu and Arabic mathematicians fare better in this respect. In modern times, the quest resulted in an interesting and rather important development in *higher arithmetic*. Like so many other chapters in the history of number theory, this one, too, began with Fermat.

Observe that the middle term of a consecutive Heronian set must be *even*, for, otherwise, the semi-perimeter, s, of the triple would not be an integer. Accordingly, we set $b = 2x$, and deduce:

$$a = 2x - 1, \; b = 2x, \; c = 2x + 1, \; 2s = 6x$$

$$s - a = x + 1, \; s - b = x, \; s - c = x - 1, \; s = 3x$$

$$T = x\sqrt{3(x^2 - 1)}$$

$$. \qquad . \qquad (14.9)$$

The problem is, therefore, to choose x in such a way that $3(x^2 - 1)$ be a *perfect square*; or—which amounts to the same thing—such that $x^2 - 1$ be of the form $3y$, where y, too, is an integer. We are thus led *to determine all integral solutions of*

$$x^2 - 3y^2 = 1 \qquad . \qquad . \qquad . \qquad (14.10)$$

Equations of this type are known as *Pell equations*. Their general form is

$$x^2 - Ry^2 = 1 \qquad . \qquad . \qquad . \qquad (14.11)$$

where R is a *non-square* integer. The strange thing is that John Pell, the obscure British mathematician after whom the equation was named, had nothing to do either with the formulation or with the solution of the problem. It was proposed by Fermat shortly before his death as a challenge to British mathematicians. We have no record of Fermat's own solution, and the one attributed to Wallis is far from satisfactory. As opposed to this, the solution given by Lagrange a hundred-odd years after the problem was proposed is a model of elegance, simplicity and rigour.

7

Lagrange derives the solution of the Pell-Fermat equation from a few elementary properties of binomials of type $x + y\sqrt{R}$, where the "modulus," R, is a *non-square* integer, while x and y are any two rational numbers. In particular, x and y may be whole numbers, and this is what we shall assume in what follows. It is convenient to present these properties in the form of lemmas:

LEMMA A. *The product of two binomials of modulus* R *is a binomial of the same modulus.* In symbols

(A) $\quad (x + y\sqrt{R})(x' + y'\sqrt{R}) = (xx' + Ryy') + (xy' + x'y)\sqrt{R}$

LEMMA B. By repeated application of lemma A we find that *the power of a binomial of modulus* R *is a binomial of the same modulus.* In symbols, if n is any positive integer, then

(B) $\qquad\qquad (x + y\sqrt{R})^n = X + Y\sqrt{R}$

where X and Y are whole numbers, provided x and y are.

Lemma C. If *two conjugate binomials* be raised to the same power, *n*, then the *resulting binomials are also conjugate*. In symbols:

(C) $(x + y\sqrt{R})^n = X + Y\sqrt{R}$ entails $(x - y\sqrt{R})^n = X - Y\sqrt{R}$

Lemma D. By combining these properties, we conclude that

(D) if $\qquad\qquad (x + y\sqrt{R})^n = X + Y\sqrt{R}$,

then $\qquad\qquad (x^2 - Ry^2)^n = X^2 - R Y^2$

This last lemma permits one to derive an infinite number of solutions to a Pell equation, if one solution is known. Assume, indeed, that p and q are two integers which satisfy the Pell equation of modulus R, i.e., that $p^2 - Rq^2 = 1$; next consider the infinite sequence of binomials

$$p_2 + q_2\sqrt{R} = (p + q\sqrt{R})^2, p_3 + q_3\sqrt{R} = (p + q\sqrt{R})^3, \text{ etc. etc.}$$

$$.\qquad.\qquad(14.12)$$

Then, in virtue of Lemma D,

$$p_2{}^2 - R q_2{}^2 = 1, p_3{}^2 - Rq_3{}^2 = 1, \ldots . p_n{}^2 - Rq_n{}^2 = 1, \ldots$$

Thus, the sets $p_2, q_2; p_3, q_3; \cdots p_n, q_n; \cdots$ are also solutions of the Pell equation of modulus R.

To illustrate, the equation $x^2 - 7y^2 = 1$ is satisfied by $x = 8$, $y = 3$. We find $(8 + 3\sqrt{7})^2 = 127 + 48\sqrt{7}$. Thus $x = 127, y = 48$ is also a solution, as may be verified directly.

Thus, *the equation* $x^2 - Ry^2 = 1$ *admits of an infinity of solutions if it admits of one*. But with this the problem is by no means settled. Two questions remain: *First*, do solutions always exist? *Second*, if they do exist, can the *Lagrange algorithm*, (14.12) generate *all* solutions from a *single basis*? Through a subtle reasoning, which has later been simplified somewhat by Gauss and Dirichlet, Lagrange proved that a *basic solution always exists, and that it is unique*, for any value of R.

To determine this basic, or *minimal*, solution for any given R is quite another matter. Thus in the case of $R = 13$, the minimal solution is $x = 649, y = 180$, while for $R = 94$, x and y contain 6 digits each. However, the quest can be greatly facilitated by the following fundamental theorem due to Euler:

If x *and* y *are solutions of the equation,* $x^2 - Ry^2 = 1$, *then* x/y *is a convergent in the expansion of* $\sqrt{R}$ *into a continued fraction.*

8

Let us now return to the problem of determining all *consecutive Heronian sets.* We saw in section 6 that the question leads to the *Pell* equation

$$x^2 - 3y^2 = 1$$

where 2x is the middle term of the triple. The *minimal* solution of this equation is, obviously, $x = 2$ $y = 1$. The Lagrange algorithm yields the binomials

$$(2 + \sqrt{3})^2 = 7 + 4\sqrt{3}, \ (2 + \sqrt{3})^3 = 26 + 15\sqrt{3}, \text{ etc. etc.}$$

The table below gives the results for the first six triples.

x	$r = y$	a	$b = 2x$	c	$T = 3xy$	x/y
2	1	3	4	5	6	F_2
7	4	13	14	15	84	F_4
26	15	51	52	53	1,170	F_6
97	56	193	194	195		F_8
362	209	723	724	725		F_{10}
1,351	780	2,701	2,702	2,703		F_{12}

It should be noted that the parameter y gives the *radius of the inscribed circle.* The last column shows the connection between these *Heronian triples* and the *convergents* to $\sqrt{3}$, listed in the preceding chapter.

Chapter Fifteen

THE CHORDS OF HIPPARCHUS

Truth: a brief holiday between two long and dreary
seasons, during the first of which it was condemned
as sophistry and during the second ignored as
commonplace.

SCHOPENHAUER

I

To one unfamiliar with the idiosyncrasies of Greek mathematicians the story which I am about to unfold will sound
quite unreal. Yet, it is just one more confirmation of the
proposition that history is no respecter of order.

In an earlier chapter I examined the conjecture that Babylonian learning had in some way penetrated into Greece
during the formative stages of geometry, a hypothesis recently
advanced to explain its prodigious progress in the three pre-
Euclidean centuries. I rejected the conjecture on the ground
that the clay tablets thus far deciphered give no more evidence
of deductive reasoning than the Egyptian papyri did.

As a matter of fact, Babylonian learning eventually did
infiltrate Greek thinking, but by then classical geometry had
been all but consummated, even as the glory of Babylon.
Indeed, the Greek who sponsored this momentous event was
the astronomer Hipparchus who flourished about 150 B.C.,
that is, at a time when Apollonius was already a mere memory,
Archimedes a legend and Euclid ancient history. As to Babylon,
the one lasting monument of its glorious past was the collection
of star calendars compiled by Chaldean priests and extending
back to times immemorial.

Hipparchus took full advantage of these Babylonian records
when he wrote his treatise on astronomy. The book was
subsequently lost, as was a similar manual by his follower
Menelaus. It is believed, however, that the essential features

of both treatises were incorporated in Ptolemy's *Almagest* which appeared about A.D. 150. Unfortunately, the Greek original of the *Almagest* has also been lost, and such parts of the work as have reached us are in the form of Latin translations of Arabic versions; and there is no telling how much of their own the zealous Arabic commentators had added to the Greek text. That these suspicions are fully justified is suggested by the very word *Almagest*, which is compounded of the Arabic article *al* and an exotic syncopation of the Greek title of the book *Megale Syntaxis*, i.e., *Grand Compendium*.

Under the circumstances, it is more than likely that many of the innovations, whether mathematical or astronomical, which have been attributed to Ptolemy were the achievements of other men. Thus, there is no doubt that it was Hipparchus who first adapted the Babylonian system to the measurement of both time and angles. These sexagesimal units were later latinized as *gradi*, *partes minutae primae* and *partes minutae secundae*; these, in turn, became the *degrees*, *minutes* and *seconds* which, for better or for worse, have survived to this day.

2

We are confronted here with the perplexing fact that Greek geometry was a finished product when the first chapter of trigonometry had not even been written. Nor, for that matter, was this first chapter ever written in Greek. The *Almagest* contained a comprehensive treatise on *spherical trigonometry*, but neither Ptolemy nor his Hindu and Arabic successors ever referred to any textbooks on *plane trigonometry*.

Now, Hipparchus, Menelaus and Ptolemy were astronomers, and their interest in *spherics* is quite understandable. What is bewildering is that these men had, apparently, plunged headlong into spherical trigonometry without using plane trigonometry as an intermediary. And yet, after all, whenever three points on a sphere define a *spherical triangle*, they also define a *plane triangle*, and it is the study of the relationship between these two species—the Greek *tripleuron* versus *trigonon*—that leads to the laws of spherical trigonometry.

Upon closer scrutiny we find that Ptolemy did make use of what we call today *plane trigonometry*, but failed to honour it with a title. Indeed, he constantly invoked the theorems and constructions of the classical geometry of triangles, as Euclid had taught it; and, in the last analysis, the formal laws so prominently displayed in our textbooks are but artful paraphrases of these classical propositions in terms of trigonometric ratios.

Thus, as I pointed out in the chapter dealing with the *hypotenuse* theorem, the so-called *law of cosines* was but a form of the extended Pythagorean proposition. The *law of half-*

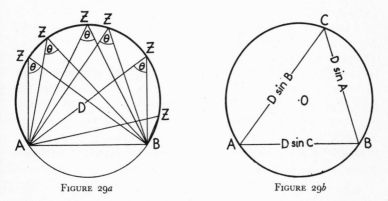

FIGURE 29a   FIGURE 29b

angles is a sort of numerical counterpart of a property of the inscribed circle, and was, as we saw, implicitly used by Hero in deriving the formula which bears his name. As to the *law of sines*, it calls for a more detailed discussion, because the *sine* was a basic concept in the Ptolemaic approach to trigonometry.

Indeed, the sine was the only one of the six trigonometrical ratios which the Greeks had honoured with a name. It was called χορδη, i.e., *the chord*. Back of this designation was the *inscribed angle theorem* which I have already mentioned on several previous occasions. In Figure 29a, UW is a fixed chord of a circle of diameter D; the vertex V of the inscribed angle is free to move along the arc subtended by the chord, but the magnitude of the inscribed angle remains *constant* throughout this motion.

It follows that this magnitude is fully determined by the *ratio of chord to diameter*; and that, conversely, the ratio k is uniquely determined by the angle θ. In short, using modern terms, k *is a function of* θ. This function the Greeks called $\chi o \rho \delta \eta$. Translated as *chorda* into Latin, it was used as a standard term until superseded by the term *sinus*.

When viewed in this light, the law of sines is an immediate corollary of the theorem that any three non-collinear points determine a unique circle. Consequently, the angles A, B, C of any triangle may be viewed as *inscribed angles* of some circle, and the corresponding sides, a, b, c, as *chords* of the same circle. If then we denote by D the diameter of that circle, we can write

$$a = D \sin A, \; b = D \sin B, \; c = D \sin C, \quad . \quad (15.1)$$

and this is the *law of sines*. (Figure 29*b*.)

This interpretation shows that the law of sines is not an exclusive attribute of the triangle, and we shall presently see that Ptolemy was fully aware of this. Indeed, the preceding argument can be extended to any *cyclic polygon*, i.e., to any polygon the vertices of which lie on one and the same circle. A case in point is the *cyclic quadrilateral* which played quite an important part in the Ptolemaic treatment.

4

We conclude that classical geometry contained all the elements required for the "solution" of triangles and rectilinear configurations generally. How about *analytic trigonometry*: the trigonometric functions of the *sum* or *difference* of two angles, of *multiples* and of *half-angles*? Well, not only were these procedures known to Ptolemy, but they were used by him with telling effect. What is more, all these calculating media were derived from a single proposition which we call today *Ptolemy's theorem*, but which the *Almagest* modestly designated as the *Lemma*.

This is the theorem: *if the four vertices of a quadrilateral are concyclic, then the sum of the products of the opposite sides is equal to the product of the diagonals of the quadrilateral.* In Figure 30,

$$\overline{AC} \cdot \overline{BD} + \overline{BC} \cdot \overline{AD} = \overline{AB} \cdot \overline{CD}. \qquad (15.2)$$

Even more remarkable than the consequences which Ptolemy drew from this property of *cyclic quadrilaterals* is the proof of the theorem. For here are displayed the same nimble virtuosity, the same apparent artfulness which we encountered in

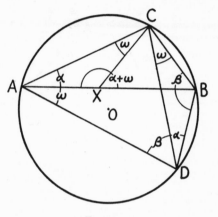

FIGURE 30

Hero's proof of the formula for the *area of a triangle*, or in Euclid's proof of the *hypotenuse theorem*. This virtuosity suggests that the proposition did not spring from the brain of an astronomer, but was the discovery of some brilliant geometer, most likely Apollonius.

As in the theorems just mentioned, it is not the proof that is hard to comprehend, but the "stratagem" behind the proof. The stratagem in this case is to determine a secant CX which partitions ABC into two triangles of which the first, ACX, is similar to CDB, and the second, BCX, is similar to CDA. This is accomplished by erecting an angle ACX equal to DCB. By the same token, angle BCX becomes equal to ACD. The rest of the proof is standard procedure: from the similitude of the two pairs of triangles we draw two proportions which, in turn, lead to the two relations,

$$\overline{CD} \cdot \overline{AX} = \overline{AC} \cdot \overline{BD} \text{ and } \overline{CD} \cdot \overline{BX} = \overline{BC} \cdot \overline{AD}.$$

Adding these and remembering that $\overline{AX} + \overline{BX} = \overline{AB}$, we obtain the theorem sought.

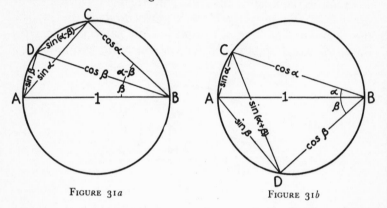

FIGURE 31a   FIGURE 31b

5

In applying the lemma to the calculation of chords, Ptolemy uses special quadrilaterals in which either a side or a diagonal coincides with a diameter of the circumscribed circle. Thus, in the case of the sum of two angles (Figure 31a), the diameter AB is a diagonal. In what follows we have replaced the Almagest terms *chord* and *complementary chord* by *sine* and *cosine*. We have also assumed the diameter of the circle to be equal to 1. Thus, one pair of opposite sides is made up of sin α and cos β, the other pair of sin β and cos α, while the second diagonal is sin $(\alpha + \beta)$. A direct application of Ptolemy's theorem leads to the *addition formula*:

$$\sin (\alpha + \beta) = \sin \alpha \cos \beta + \sin \beta \cos \alpha \quad . \quad (15.3)$$

In Figure 31b, the diameter of the circle is taken for one of the sides. Ptolemy's theorem then yields the *difference* formula

$$\sin (\alpha - \beta) = \sin \alpha \cos \beta - \sin \beta \cos \alpha \quad . \quad (15.4)$$

Finally, Figure 32 shows how Ptolemy handled the *dichotomy* problem; *the chord of an angle being given, calculate the chord of the half-angle.* Here the chords $\overline{DB}$ and $\overline{DC}$ are equal, their

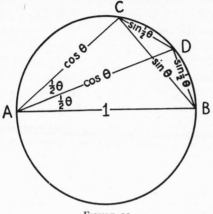

FIGURE 32

common length being $\sin \frac{1}{2}\theta$; the chord BC is $\sin \theta$, and the diagonal $\overline{AD}$ is $\cos \theta$. Thus

$$\sin \tfrac{1}{2}\theta + \sin \tfrac{1}{2}\theta \cos \theta = \cos \tfrac{1}{2}\theta \sin \theta$$

This, in turn, leads to the *dichotomy formula*

$$\tan \tfrac{1}{2}\theta = \operatorname{cosec} \theta - \cot \theta \quad . \qquad . \quad (15.5)$$

which, incidentally, was used by Archimedes four hundred years earlier for the computation of π.

6

These principles were applied in the *Almagest* to the computation of a *table of chords*, which, from all accounts, was largely a reproduction of the one appended to the lost treatise of Hipparchus, a circumstance that casts added doubt on the authorship of the theorem which bears Ptolemy's name. The table is of great historical interest, not only because it was the first of its kind, but because its very conception was a radical departure from classical tradition. Besides, it offers an insight into the difficulties with which calculators of that period were beset.

To bring these handicaps out in sharper relief I shall present here in outline Ptolemy's calculation of the *sine of one degree. Step I.* The sine and cosine of 18° were taken directly from the *golden section* triangle. (See Chapter Five and Figure 8.) *Step II.* The functions of 15° were derived from those of 30° by *dichotomy. Step III.* The functions of 3° were derived from those of 18° and 15° by means of the *difference formula* (15.4). *Step IV.* The functions of $1\frac{1}{2}°$ and of $\frac{3}{4}°$ were obtained from those of 3° by two consecutive *dichotomies. Step V.* Finally, the sine of 1° was derived from the sines of $1\frac{1}{2}°$ and $\frac{3}{4}°$ by *interpolation.*

The latter was based on an inequality which had already been used by the astronomer Aristarchus, a contemporary of Archimedes. In fact, one commentator attributes it to Hippias of Elis, which is not so far fetched as it may first appear, inasmuch as it is, in a sense, suggested by the quadratrix. Indeed, the quadratrix is represented by the function $x/\tan x$ whereas the inequality back of Ptolemy's interpolation deals with the related function $\sin x/x$.

7

Figure 33 is the graph of $y = \sin x/x$. Observe that the function is *steadily decreasing* as x varies from 0 to π. This means that if α, θ and β are three consecutive values of x, then

$$\frac{\sin \alpha}{\alpha} > \frac{\sin \theta}{\theta} > \frac{\sin \beta}{\beta}$$

from which we draw *the inequality used by Ptolemy*:

$$\frac{\theta}{\alpha} \sin \alpha > \sin \theta > \frac{\theta}{\beta} \sin \beta \qquad . \qquad . \qquad (15.6)$$

In the second place, the function attains a *maximum* for $x = 0$, which means that for small values of x, the curve is quite "flat." Thus, the interval between $\sin \alpha / \alpha$ and $\sin \beta / \beta$ is small, if α and β are small, and this is what accounts for the extraordinary precision of the method.

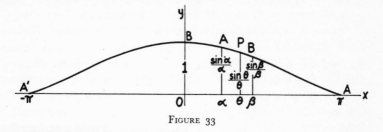

We find, indeed, by applying the inequality to $\alpha = 90'$, $\theta = 60'$ and $\beta = 45'$, that

$$\frac{2}{3} \sin 90' > \sin 60' > \frac{4}{3} \sin 45',$$

i.e.,

$$0 \cdot 01745 \ldots > \sin 1° > 0 \cdot 01745$$

We are thus justified in taking $\sin 1° = 0 \cdot 01745$, which agrees with the value drawn from a *five place* table. It also agrees quite closely with the value given in the *Almagest* table: $\sin 1° = 1' 3''$.

Let me say here for the benefit of the puzzled reader that along with the Babylonian measures of time and angles, Hipparchus adopted the so-called *sexigesimal fractions*. Thus, $1' 3''$ meant $1/60 + 3/3600$. Ptolemy followed suit, and, as a matter of fact, this method of writing fractions was in common use even in the days of Copernicus. However cumbersome this notation may appear to us today, it was in keeping with the spirit of the time, and may indeed be viewed as a *precursor* of the *decimal fraction* which in its present form is barely three hundred years old.*

And while on the subject of notation let me add that the terminology and symbols used in trigonometry today are largely those which Euler had introduced about two hundred years ago. The earlier nomenclature and notation were in

* See this author's *Number, the Language of Science*, 4th edition, Allen & Unwin, 1954. Pages 257 and 258.

many respects as inarticulate and as awkward as those used by Ptolemy and his Arabic and Hindu successors.

8

The essential difference between the classical geometry of the triangle, as Euclid taught it, and the trigonometry of Hipparchus can be summed up in a single word, *goniometry*. Without goniometry, trigonometric ratios are but empty symbols and trigonometric laws fruitless formalities. The ratios are raised to the dignity of functions, and the laws acquire universal significance through a principle which *co-ordinates angular measurement with the measurement of lengths*. Such a principle, in turn, rests on the assumption that *it is possible to establish a one-to-one correspondence between the arcs of a circle and the segments of a line.*

Classical geometry had no goniometry in this broad sense of the term. The *Elements* of Euclid defined congruent angles; defined addition and subtraction of angles; the multiples of an angle; dichotomy. It taught how to divide a complete revolution into 3, 5 and 15 parts, and how to subdivide any angle into 2^n parts. Still, all these definitions and constructions were strictly *operational*, and the operations were restricted to manipulations *by straightedge and compass*. To solve a triangle was a *graphical* problem which, generally, had *no arithmetic counterpart*.

Classical geometry had an angular unit: the *right angle* or *quadrant*. But only such fractions of the quadrant were recognized as *bona fide* angles as could be reached by *cyclotomy*; any others, such as 1/7, 1/9 or 1/90, were outside the "angular pale." And such was the power of the interdiction imposed by the *"divine instruments,"* that even a Eudoxus or an Archimedes could not shake off these inhibitions.

Then an astronomer rushed in where geometers had feared to tread. Not content with foisting on classical geometry an unwanted goniometry, he added insult to injury by defying the sacred rules of *cyclotomy*. Any goniometry which accepted the general angle at par with the "cyclotomic" was a radical departure from Greek tradition. Still, Hipparchus could have preserved a modicum of classical decorum by adopting for unit some angle within the scope of the *divine instruments*, such as 1/60, 1/80 or 1/96 of a quadrant, in lieu of the Babylonian 1/90, which lay outside the "pale." It was a choice between a Greek schism and a Babylonian heresy. Hipparchus chose heresy.

EPILOGUE

Not yet has man learned how to celebrate his highest attainments.

NIETZSCHE

I

What is the scope of the Greek contribution? What place should the historian assign to the Greeks in the evolution of mathematical thought and technique? Is the statement "in mathematics all roads lead back to Hellas" a just appraisal, or just a specious metaphor? Was it devotion to Greek principles that brought about the prodigious progress of the last few centuries, or was it renunciation of Greek mathematical taboos?

As I ponder over these questions, there come to my mind the words of Poincaré: "To doubt all or all believe are two equally convenient solutions, in that both dispense with thinking."

2

My account of the Greek Bequest touched on many problems and issues, which had their reverberations in modern times; and yet, it is not the whole story. A number of equally important achievements had to be relegated to the next volume of this trilogy. Lack of space was one reason for this deferment. The other was my feeling that these issues could be presented in sharper relief when etched against the background of the time and the place where they had attained fruition.

Among these topics will be such significant achievements as the *quadratures* of Archimedes which anticipated the *integral calculus* of Newton by two thousand years; the *Conics* of Apollonius which foreshadowed the *analytic geometry* of Descartes; the *porisms* of Euclid and Pappus which contained the germs of the *projective geometry* of Desargues; the *Arithmetica* of Diophantus which inspired the *number-theoretical* discoveries of Fermat; the *principle of exhaustion*; the *postulate of parallels*; the *curves* of Diocles and Nicomedes; Euclid's brilliant studies in *prime and perfect numbers*.

An imposing array, yet all parts of the mathematical heritage bequeathed to us by the Greeks. If these topics be ranged alongside of those recorded in the present volume, the list would read like a table of contents of an encyclopedia of modern mathematics. By the same token, the words "all roads lead back to Greece" would resound like an apt description of the relation between classical and modern mathematics.

3

When, however, we examine closer the twelve odd centuries which separate the end of the classical from the beginning of the modern era, we find this metaphoric appraisal specious, to say the least. The first eight centuries of that period are known as the *Dark Ages*. There has been a tendency in recent years to avoid this term, but I know of no more fitting epithet unless it be *interminable night*. There were no roads leading to Hellas in that barren wasteland. Just trails littered with the ruins of Greek culture. Occasionally an errant monk would stalk among the ruins in vain search of a Greek *rationale* which would vindicate his wild obsession. And that was all.

When at long last the obsession had run its course, there came to Western Europe a magnificent upsurge known as the *Renaissance*. Pent-up energy released found creative outlets in the *arts*, in *letters*, in *music* and *philosophy*. However, there was no corresponding upsurge in mathematics at that time. Feeble attempts were made to revive Greek classics through Latin translations of their Arabic versions, but these efforts had no lasting effect. Indeed, the only mathematician of the period worthy of the name was Fibonacci, and he was more interested in spreading Arabic ideas than in restoring the glory of Greece.

4

Then came the *seventeenth century* and an upsurge which, for intensity and extent, had no equal in the annals of mathematics. Most of the subjects which grace the mathematical curriculum of a modern college came into being during that period. *Geometry, analytical, projective, infinitesimal; theory of equations* and *number theory; the calculus, theory of functions, infinite series, theory of curves; probabilities, theoretical and celestial mechanics.*

Now, all this happened in less than one hundred years. Indeed, while the *Isagogs* of Vieta, which ushered in the new era, had appeared in 1592, the full significance of his symbolism was not realized until after the author's mysterious death in 1603. On the other hand, in 1686, when Newton's *Principia Mathematica* was published, the new mathematics was already a *fait accompli*. Thus, measured by contemporary standards, there was more ground covered in this, *the first*, century of modern mathematics than during the nearly one thousand years which separate Thales from Pappus. Why?

We certainly cannot ascribe this prodigious progress to the superior ability of the mathematicians of the seventeenth century, or to their deeper insight. The phenomenal virtuosity of the Greek masters and their almost uncanny intuition speak for themselves. Indeed, so circumscribed were the methods of the classical era, that almost any new problem called for a *tour de force* which only a virtuoso could perform. Again, to say that Fermat, Descartes or Newton had tools available which were not known to the Greeks is begging the question, inasmuch as these tools were forged by the very men who used them. What were the stimuli that urged these men on, stimuli which, apparently, did not exist in the Greek era?

5

What classical mathematics needed to become an organized whole, and to qualify, at the same time, as spokesman of the sciences which lean on it for counsel and approval, was not more or greater men of genius, and not new principles or concepts: *it needed a new language.* Does this mean that the Latin of Descartes and Newton was better adapted to express mathematical thought than the Greek of Apollonius or Pappus? No, indeed! The question as to which of the sundry languages evolved by civilization could best serve the needs of mathematics is of no historical significance, since the verdict of history has been that no such language can ever fill the exacting demands of mathematics.

As I write these lines, I think of the cynical phrase of Talleyrand: "Speech has been given to man that he may disguise his thoughts." A choleric historian might paraphrase this into: *"Speech has been inflicted on man to obscure thought, paralyse action and impede progress,"* and could invoke the story of classical mathematics to confirm his words. A more benign interpreter of human history would counter: "Language is not a gift of Providence. It grew out of the needs of a social being to convey to other such beings his wishes, entreaties and commands; to share with other such beings his hopes and fears; to implore, placate, cajole and exorcise the mystic forces which controlled his destiny. It antedates inference and deduction by countless eons; it bears the indelible imprints of the chaotic mist through which human intuition was groping, ages before the advent of reason."

6

Thales of Miletus armed intuition with a brain, and out of the nebulous mist emerged mathematics. But neither Thales nor his followers armed the thinker with an organ of speech which would fittingly express his thoughts, subtle yet precise, or describe the countless forms which his imagination could conjure up. Greek mathematics had to depend on common speech, a medium replete with ambiguities, yet inflexible; open to inconsistencies which it could not detect; where an interchange of words could jeopardize meaning, and where emphasis could be attained only through intonation. These were the handicaps under which Greek mathematics laboured throughout the thousand years of its existence.

And then, as though by magic, mathematics was freed from the vagaries of human speech and presented with a language all its own. I use the word *magic* advisedly, for, the most striking feature of the event was the spontaneity and rapidity of this transition from the old mathematics to the new. It began at the threshold of the century, and by 1650 the new medium had already infiltrated into practically every field of mathematics, pure or applied.

Whenever I reflect on that epical transition, there comes to my mind the legend of Hesiod, according to which Zeus had swallowed his wife Metis when she was pregnant with Athena, acting on a warning that his children by her might prove stronger than himself and dethrone him. But Prometheus split open the head of Zeus, and Athena sprang forth fully armed and uttering a loud shout of victory. Prometheus was not aware of the enormous potentialities of the liberated goddess. And neither was Vieta, the Prometheus of Mathematics, aware of the revolutionary outcome of his discovery. Indeed, had he been so aware, he would have hailed the discovery as *lingua mathematica*, instead of christening it with the vapid name of *logistica speciosa*.

7

"Not yet has man learned how to celebrate his highest attainments." How fittingly these words of Nietzsche apply to the history of mathematics! The two epoch-making events in that history were the principle of *deductive reasoning* inaugurated by Thales and the *symbolic algebra* of Vieta. Yet, not only do we not commemorate these events, and not only have the men to whom we owe these achievements been all but forgotten, but we even lack names to identify these achievements for what they are.

Indeed, few of our textbooks mention the Vieta discovery at all, and those that do, identify it as *literal notation*, a term which is not only pointless, but actually deceptive, since the use of the letters of an alphabet for symbols is wholly irrelevant, and the idiom is certainly more than a mere notation. In fact, even the term language does not adequately describe the scope and power of the medium. For, while the idiom will discharge the principal functions of any written language, it will also perform feats which even the most eloquent orator or the most inspired poet cannot hope to attain.

Thus, the change of structure in a sentence will, as a rule, destroy the intended meaning, or, at best, produce a *pun*, even if the rules of *grammar* have been strictly obeyed. On the other hand, in a symbolic relation a transformation which conforms to the laws of *algebra* reveals the equivalence of two forms, and this means a *theorem* in the field which has marshalled these symbols to its aid.

Again, when words in a sentence are given a new connotation, the result is an *ambiguity*, or, at best, a *metaphor*. But if a symbolic relation is valid in two distinct fields, then any consequence of the relation in one of the fields has its counterpart in the other. Such *isomorphisms* have led to many valuable discoveries in applied mathematics.

Finally, if the words of a sentence are subject to certain reservations, then to disregard these restrictions means to risk grave consequences; indeed, we owe most of our errors to just such abuse. On the other hand, a symbolic relation in which the entities involved have originally been *restricted in type or range* will often retain its meaning when the restriction is removed and thus lead to fruitful *generalizations*. The evolution of the number concept from integer to vector is a case in point.

This, then, is the historical significance of Vieta's discovery: it not only endowed mathematics with a language, but armed it with such powerful weapons as *paraphrase, analogy, generalization*. Thus did Vieta turn a tongue-tied thinker into a fluent and convincing speaker, and, at the same time, immensely enriched the thinker's creative and critical faculties.

8

The publication in 1630 of Galileo's *Dialogues on the Two New Sciences* provided a second powerful stimulus to the mathematics of the seventeenth century. In that work Galileo sought to extend the notion of velocity to *non-uniform motion*. He inquired: what would happen to the *average speed* of a moving particle when the time-interval was gradually reduced? This led him to the concept of *instantaneous velocity*. The latter he defined as the *limit* towards which the average speed *tends* when the time-interval *diminished indefinitely*, which, of course, was in all but name the *derivative of space with respect to time*.

It was another case of an astronomer rushing in where geometers feared to tread. The spell was broken: Fermat was quick to adopt the new ideas to geometry; a veritable orgy of applications followed, and *infinitesimal analysis* was born. *Infinite processes, infinitesimals, limits*—concepts which Greek geometers had shunned with a circumspection akin to awe— were henceforth to be used as legitimate instruments of mathematical reasoning and technique. Thus did Galileo inadvertently cut the Gordian knot of a taboo which had plagued mathematics since its inception.

Still, the enormous success of infinitesimal analysis should not blind the historian to the fact that the discipline owed its existence not to a new conception, but to a bold overt break with an age-old tradition. We should also remember that Greek mathematical history is studded with attempts to shake off the taboos imposed by that tradition; that these attempts, timid and disguised at first, were becoming more resolute as mathematics advanced; and that the *Collection* of Pappus is interspersed with problems where the infinite with its sundry ramifications was used directly, even if not explicitly.

9

The Greek title of the Pappus work was *Synagogs*, which stood for *collection* or *assembly*. Quite a fitting title, too, for, here

Pappus assembled a veritable pageant of classical problems, ranging from the earliest days of Greek geometry to his own times. Some were old questions in a new guise, others were, undoubtedly, due to Pappus himself, but all bear the elegant touch of a master mathematician and skilful teacher. Indeed, the very style and arrangement of the material suggest that he had been the head of a school of high standing.

The historical significance of the *Synagogs* is that it serves as the best available source on the scope and ken of those mathematical classics which had perished during the Dark Ages, and, at the same time, sheds light on the state of mathematics at the eve of the *blackout*. But it does more than that. For, by revealing the trends of mathematical thought and technique at the close of the classical era, it brings out in true perspective the transition from the old mathematics to the new.

The juxtaposition of the two works, the *Synagogs* of Pappus, that swan song of classical mathematics, and the *Isagogs* of Vieta, the first significant book of the modern era, would disclose the origin of many current ideas, and would, at the same time, clear up many perplexing historical questions. This is the reason why I have deferred the study of the closing era of Greek mathematics to the next volume of this trilogy. Still, the era is a part of the classical panorama: hence, a fitting climax to a story of the *Greek Bequest*. And so I shall close my narrative with a retrospective glance at that crucial era in the history of man, when the fate of thought was hanging in the balance.

10

History may be likened to one of those tapestries of intricate weave in which an eye can discern almost any design conceived in advance, any one at variance with any other, yet none conflicting with the whole.

One might picture the death scene of Hellenism as a host of saints chanting *Hosannas* on the grave of a pagan who had died in despair and decay from hypertrophy of the mind and atrophy of the soul. Or, one might picture it as a horde of fanatics massed under the banner of *ratio delenda est*, glaring with glee at a prostrate Prometheus, felled at the prime of life. Between these extremes one might intercalate a variety of other designs, no two agreeing with each other, yet, every one drawing aid and comfort from the confusing accounts of an age of much heat and no light.

A bewildering freedom of choice, but, actually, no freedom, since one's choice is predicated by one's temperament, upbringing and entourage. Nor is the historian free from such bias, and I, for one, have never concealed my own. *Homo sum et humanum nihil a me alienum puto.*

Many centuries lie between us and those tragic days, but the ideological conflict between the *Hellenists* and the *apologists* has not abated. The one speaks of the event as of darkness engulfing light and regards modern progress as the reincarnation of Hellenism; the other describes the end of Greek culture in terms of degeneracy, decadence, decline and decay.

I do not feel competent to weigh the merits of the controversy in fields other than my own. However, I did make an honest effort to appraise the mathematics of that era. I read and re-read the *Metrica* of Hero, the *Almagest* of Ptolemy, the *Arithmetica* of Diophantus, the *Collection* of Pappus, and sundry other works which had escaped the vigilance of the saints. I found there a growing understanding of the issues which had stalled their mathematical predecessors, and a groping for means to resolve these issues. I found pride of achievement, and prouder yet visions of conquests to come. But nowhere did I detect evidence of decay or traces of decline. Yes, I, too, have scanned that intricate weave to discern the stage on which had been enacted the last hours of classical mathematics, and here is what I saw from where I stood:

A bright day was shining, lofty vistas were looming, fresh breezes were scattering the cobwebs of ancient taboos, when the lights went out, and the curtain of history dropped on the Grand Drama of Hellas.

INDEX